Neighbors

A Crack the Spine Themed Anthology

Published by Crack the Spine

Edited by Kerri Farrell Foley

Collection Copyright © 2020 Crack the Spine

Individual works are the sole property of the authors

Crack the Spine is a production of Quartermarch Media, LLC

ISBN-13: 978-1-7328693-2-5
ISSN: 2474-9095

CONTENTS

LETTER FROM THE EDITOR

We selected the theme of "Neighbors" for this anthology to explore the concept of community. While the traditional impressions of neighbors most commonly involve thoughts of proximity, we also found that neighbors need not be nearby to be a part of our community. The stories, poems, and essays in this collection explore themes of identity, equality, tension, and discord. The authors in these pages fearlessly explore the broad concepts implicit in the simple word "neighbors" and they emerge with insights both inspiring and heart-breaking. It has been my honor to edit this anthology, and by reading it, you, the reader, have become a part of our community. We're neighbors now.

Kerri Farrell Foley

MY NEIGHBOR'S SON

REBEKAH KEATON

The heavy stroke of your howl
on my skin shows,
in city neighborhoods
we live close.

I measure
the lengths of your breath
like the paper chain links
of Mr. Geiser's second grade,
circling double around the room.

A month's labor, and we triumphantly trailed
the alternating green and red construction down the hall
in contest with the other second grades,
high on Elmer's paste and the taste of early competition.

At the end of the week, in Mrs. Harris' Sunday school class,
we sang *Happy Birthday Jesus,* stuck out our tongues,
went straight for the icing.

Your cry sounds to me like the rising chords
of *Jesus Loves Me*, a child's chain
winding around and around this neighborhood, my yard,
my deck chair where I sit, knees bent.

HERO

ANN CWIKLINSKI

"Excuse me, Miss."

Great. That big guy making a beeline for Nessa is determined to interrupt the only moment of peace she's had all day—if you call sitting on a scratchy, stain-resistant armchair in the optometrist's waiting room, thumbing through a year-old *Time* magazine, "peace". She's been racing around ever since she left work an hour ago—picking up her daughter from gymnastics at one end of town, pulling her protesting boys early from baseball practice at the other end, dropping them all with the neighbor to whom she already owes too many favors, sprinting through the grocery store to grab a frozen pizza and milk for supper (and shoving the groceries under a blanket in the back of the car in an optimistic attempt to insulate them against 80-degree heat for the next hour), speeding to the optometrist's office, and bursting into the reception area 5 minutes late—forfeiting her 6:00 appointment to a delighted woman in a floral top practically skipping her way down the hall to the examining room, exclaiming about her good fortune at nabbing the earlier appointment.

Just a minute to breathe, that's all Nessa wants.

But this guy apparently needs something. She sizes him up as he approaches her: A tall, black man, strongly built; definitely not young, but hard to guess how old with his face half obscured by a forward-tipped Orioles cap and aviator sunglasses—almost like he's trying to hide something. He's walking a little funny, too, sort of stumbling—like that groundhog that wouldn't get away from the back porch last week. Not drunk or anything—he's too stiff-legged for drunk—but maybe... hurt in some way.

The man grips the back of the chair next to Nessa's and extends his phone toward her, as if he wants his picture taken—although the humdrum waiting room, with its institutional blue-flecked wallpaper and grid of slightly crooked diplomas covering one wall, strikes Nessa as a peculiar backdrop for a photo. The three women sitting across the small room, instantly blasé to the celebrity gossip in *People* and indifferent to the health tips in *Arthritis Today*, peek up from their magazines. One—elderly, white, and severely myopic, judging from her thick, lavender-framed glasses—tugs at the fat purse stowed on the seat beside her in what seems more a mistrustful reflex than an earnest offer of a seat. The other two women, also white, but a little younger—by optometric measures, probably midway between reading glasses and cataracts—also sit a little more stiffly, alert even as they lower their gazes back to their magazines.

"Excuse me, Miss, do you text?" the man asks, leaning over Nessa.

"Text?"

"I've got to text my daughter but I can't see the letters."

He sounds as desperate as he does polite, so Nessa drops her magazine, lays his phone across her palm, and taps keys as he dictates: "Left hospital. At eye doctor. Please call."

Nessa, farsighted herself, holds out the small screen to proofread, but the man urges, "Send it! Just send it!" so she pokes a likely-looking green icon. The man's hand shakes as he retrieves his phone and stuffs it into the pocket of his rumpled chinos. He eases himself into the chair beside Nessa, grimacing as he sinks onto the cushion.

That daughter better call, thinks Nessa.

The man pulls off his cap, revealing a white, grown-out buzz cut, and hangs it on his knee. He hooks his sunglasses over the neck of his t-shirt and leans back in his chair wearily. Nessa can now see that his right eye is squeezed shut, the skin around it swollen and bruised and abraded—a pulpy, purplish-red. "Wine-dark" pops into her head, a Homeric phrase that carries with it, especially under these circumstances, the peripheral, shadowy image of the blind poet. God, let him not go blind in that eye, Nessa thinks, wincing. A few years back, her youngest son took a sharp stick to the eye during an ill-considered duel with an excitable friend. In a panic, she raced him to the ophthalmologist, and watched anxiously as the doctor probed for permanent damage. Unable to soothe her howling son, Nessa offered frantic, mute prayers to remote saints reputedly sympathetic to the blind and maimed. The doctor, after finally medicating and bandaging the eye, grimly warned her son not to run, jump, read, or watch television for two weeks. Nessa spent the next 14 days at her son's bedside, reading him stories with an urgency that rivaled Scheherazade's, until his rust-red iris faded back to its usual shade of pale green, and his stunned pupil relaxed its crazed, manga dimensions.

"Thank you, Miss," the wounded man sighs as he tries to settle himself more comfortably in his chair.

"That looks painful," Nessa observes cautiously, unsure if it is ruder to pry or to ignore an obvious injury.

"Sure is. Hope the doctor can fix me up." He pauses. "If I can't see, I can't work: I'm a hack."

"A cab driver?"

"Yep. I couldn't work today, and it looks like I won't be working tomorrow."

"Oh, dear."

Without admitting concern for himself, the man continues, "A lot of people count on me to shuttle them around. I have these two sisters I pick up at 5 every morning, drive home at 5 every night. They work at that chicken factory north of town. Only been in the country a year. They're from … Guatemala, I think. Someplace warm and beautiful, anyway; they miss it something awful. They have family back home to support, so I only charge them a few bucks. How are they gonna get to work?"

Nessa pictures the sisters bundled up against unfamiliar morning cold, yawning in the back seat of his cab, confiding their homesickness to this big man they've come to trust. How *are* they going to get to work?

He continues, "My daughter wants me to quit working—I'm 74—but I like helping people out, seeing what's going on downtown. And I want to put something aside for my grandson…" He trails off, not ready to contemplate the ramifications of a serious eye injury.

"Did you have an accident?" Nessa asks.

"It wasn't no accident," he snorts. "I stopped for a quart of milk at Minit Mart on the way home after my last fare last night—not late, maybe 9 o'clock—and some kids were hanging around, harassing the girl at the checkout. Troublemakers with nothing better to do. The girl looked upset, so I tried to distract them, said, 'Shouldn't you be outside selling dope with your buddies?'"

Nessa winces. Because Homer is already haunting her imagination, and because the cabdriver was apparently waylaid on his way home after a long day roaming the city, she thinks of wandering Odysseus and his foolhardy jibes at the Cyclops—a sloppy comparison, really, considering her new friend resembles both the imprudent hero and, with his ocular injury, the one-eyed giant of the story.

She says, "I wouldn't dare take on a gang of kids like that!"

"And you shouldn't. But I'm not afraid of them. I'm old, but I'm big. And stupid, you're probably thinking, but I always try to talk

6

sense to the kids in the neighborhood. Convince 'em to stay out of trouble. Most of them respect me." He shakes his head. "Not these characters, though: they followed me outside, and the biggest one hit me, hard, right here." He gingerly touches his swollen eyelid. "I blacked out, woke up in an ambulance."

"Oh, I am so sorry," Nessa says. "You want me to try your daughter again?"

"No, she's probably busy. She's a nurse. She'll answer when she answers…"

"Well, the doctor here is wonderful," Nessa tries to comfort him. "He mended my son's eye after his accident. He had to lie still for two weeks—the doctor will probably insist you do that—but he regained 20-20 vision. He's even a pretty good artist…" She is babbling nervously now; when the man screws his good eye closed, she figures he is feigning sleep to shut her up.

In fact, one of her agitated gestures has caught his attention.

"Do that again!" he says.

"What?"

"Flap your hand around."

With his good eye still closed, he squints through his swollen eyelid at Nessa's waving hand.

"I can see something moving! This morning I couldn't see nothing!"

He covers his face with his broad hands. Only when he brushes his fingertips across his eyelids does Nessa realize he is crying.

"Sorry, sorry," he says, dropping his hands and squaring his shoulders.

"That's o.k.," Nessa assures him, patting his arm. "Tears are balm for that eye…" But a familiar panic flutters up at the thought of him losing his sight, his job, his independence. She sends a fierce telepathic message to Saint Lucy, patron saint of eye injuries, although

7

she fears that demanding intercession for a second miracle in 2 years might be frowned upon in saintly circles. She quickly appends a belated but sincere prayer of gratitude for her son's recovery.

"Roger?" calls a young woman in blue scrubs precisely matched to the wallpaper in the waiting room. The man grabs his hat off his knee and hoists himself up. "Thank you, Miss," he says again to Nessa. "You take care now." He limps down the hall after the woman, past a row of mistily-Impressionistic landscape posters, elaborately framed like tributes to myopia.

As he disappears around the corner, one of the magazine-reading women declares, "So glad I moved out of the city. I used to live two blocks from that Minit Mart. Kids hanging out there all the time. Late, too. Should be a curfew."

The woman beside her agrees emphatically before sharing a long story of a nephew who swallowed two teeth when he was mugged outside a city bar. Within weeks, she reports, he fled to the suburbs, where he presumably lived happily-gap-toothed ever after.

The third woman boasts of her nearby small town—so safe—and neighbors—so friendly. "Of course, you can't buy a quart of milk after 8 o'clock, but if that's the price you pay for safety, well... I'm willing to pay it!" she crows. The other women nod vigorously: Late-night dairy products be damned!

Not once do they mention the injured man. They seem untroubled that somebody's father, somebody's grandfather, was beaten to a pulp by kids with problems of their own. Like a bespectacled Greek chorus, unscathed by drama unfolding around them, they instead sing the virtues of side-stepping violence.

Which hardly seems heroic.

Tired as she is, Nessa abruptly jumps off her chair, runs out to her car, fetches a half-gallon of milk from her bag of groceries, and sprints back to the office. She sits with the sweating carton on her lap as the magazine women exchanged bemused glances. When the man, his eye neatly bandaged, emerges from the examining room and goes to settle his bill, Nessa sidles up to him and plunks the carton on the receptionist's high counter.

"Here. I assume you spilled your milk all over the Minit Mart parking lot," she says. "I can give you a ride home after my checkup."

"My daughter's on her way, but thank you, Miss," he assures her. "You know, it's just like you said: I have to lie still awhile, but I'll recover."

His spirits are already on the mend. He grabs the milk carton and swings it up high. "To human kindness," he jokes.

Such an underrated virtue, Nessa thinks. Not worthy of epic, maybe, but much better than indifference. Or perhaps generous gestures—defending frightened cashiers, befriending recent immigrants—do glow ever so faintly with mythic heroism....

"To kindness," she agrees.

TAMING WHAT INFESTS US

PERI DWYER WORRELL

Invaded, a pouch, a crease, a sulcus
Tiny entities that do not matter do
Matter now that they have bred
Though you never took them in.

Nothing to do now but love them
A boy in a tenement's pets
Six legs, racing roaches in jars
Pigeons, rats, mitochondria.

Here, parrots flock and strip
Fruit from the trees and sing
In cages on the porch. Know
What's yours is never and always theirs.

OUTSIDE

ELLEN WEEREN

Elizabeth's phone buzzed with the familiar ding of something happening. An ant was crawling across the camera's lens. An hour later she checked the app and a majestic blue bird flew by with an urgency she couldn't manage for herself. The camera turned itself off.

It was a Sunday but that didn't make much difference. Every day might as well have been a Sunday. She gathered the empty black olive can by her chair and stuffed it deep into the kitchen trash. Then she pulled the red strings tight and tied them in a triple knot.

"No time like the present," her mother always said.

She opened the front door. Three girls who were about twelve stood close together in the cul-de-sac. She watched them—and they watched her—as she crossed her driveway to the receptacles on the side of her garage. Like an owl, she kept her eyes wide open and turned in their direction. Clearly unsettled, they looked at their phones and then to the woods on the other side of her house.

"You girls need some help?" She waved and gave them what she hoped came across as a warm smile.

She recognized the Johnson girl. Her sister had been friends with Elizabeth's daughter. Elizabeth's son had coached the Johnson kids on the neighborhood swim team. They were a bit too complicated for Elizabeth's liking but nice enough to chat with during a meet. She missed those swim meets.

"A man was chasing us," they answered in unison. "We're looking for our friends."

"You have your phone—let's call them." Elizabeth's throat seized up. Her heart beat fast.

The redhead touched her screen and said, "Two of them are near the pool looking for Alison."

Elizabeth walked the three over to the pool just behind her house. Their two friends waited in the parking lot. A third girl walked alone from the wooded path.

The girls all pointed to her. "There's Alison."

Relief waved over them like a mirage, fuzzy but still welcome.

When she had them altogether, Elizabeth said, "You girls must never be alone in a situation like this. Always stick together."

A guy dressed in black had come out of nowhere and chased them, the girls told Elizabeth. He grunted but did not speak. He was tall and skinny. Older than high school but probably not thirty. They'd never seen him before. No one had been touched or harmed.

Elizabeth felt shaky.

"Well that makes me nervous just hearing about it. Y'all handled that quite well." She wanted to gather the girls in a hug but thought it would probably make them more uncomfortable. "But next time you should call 911 immediately."

"We thought about that," the redhead said. "But we didn't think they'd believe us."

Elizabeth knew that story. Her brother's best friend had tried to kiss her on the mouth when she was eight. His tongue had been thick and slug-like, slimy against her lips. She only got away by kicking him in the nuts. When she told her mother about it, she said, "Oh honey, that's a compliment. It means he thinks you're pretty."

These girls were pretty, too. Elizabeth's face flushed with anger that all this time later another girl would be chased by another boy. It felt like a bad cartoon on a loop.

She called the police and had each girl call her mother. Then she waited with them until every girl had a parent present.

One mother walked over to Elizabeth and said, "What would they have done without you? Thank you for being there."

"You're a godsend," another mother added.

"Oh it's nothing. My pleasure." Her face now pink with pride. "I'm going to go back and check my doorbell video. Maybe it caught something."

"Thank yous," echoed behind her as if a small parade had been gathered in her honor.

The doorbell hadn't captured the aggressor, only the girls running from him.

Elizabeth opened another can of olives and poured herself a ginger ale with a sprig of mint and lots of ice. *This is an afternoon for something bubbly.* She was almost giddy.

She took the olives and the soda to the front porch where she sat and waited for the next great thing to happen.

RETURN RIDE

JAMES B. NICOLA

When last I rode this country road,
its window drapes all drawn,
    about one in ten
    were adjusted when
I passed by. (I kept on.)

Out of a hundred, seven showed
a face beyond the glass.
    And a hand might wave
    at a glance I gave,
or a head nod. (And I'd pass.)

It's now an interstate, and both
its shoulders sport a fence
    to keep sounds and fumes
    from the grounds and rooms.
Above, the air is dense

with forty years of bows and growth
which shiver as trucks whiz below.
    And were you to look through
    a pane I once knew,
why, I would never know.

A HOUSE WITH NO WALLS

ANNABELLE BLOMELEY

It happened on the second day of July when the air was sticky and the sea breezes welcoming. All of the neighbors were talking about it, standing at the edge of their yards and exchanging quick, deep whispers, always looking over their shoulders. They kept asking each other why, and how, and who, and all the questions they knew no one could begin to answer. One couldn't blame them though, because not even the Peterses-- who happened to own the big, white house where it had occurred-- knew what was going on. Mrs. Peters figured they had been cursed, probably by the new maid they had already fired. Little Ricky Peters figured it was magic, while his older sister, Emilia, could barely even bring herself to think of it. Mr. Peters acted like it wasn't even happening, which is very hard to do when the walls of your house start to unexplainably disappear.

The first wall to leave was one of Emilia's bedroom walls, which was painted yellow and had two windows and just so happened to face the street. Emilia had woken up feeling very cold and she could hear the wind much more than she was used to. The seagulls were shrieking outside, flapping their wings at each other in the wind.

When Emilia sat up and saw straight out of her bedroom, she couldn't do anything but scream. She thought she was dreaming, so she got out of bed and quickly walked to where the wall should have been, looking down the one-story drop as if it was a cliff. Emilia had always hated the smell of the salty air ever since she moved down to Apalachicola, it reminded her of fish and their bulging eyes. She screamed again, and her father, mother, and brother ran to her room.

Mr. Peters had a few choice words upon looking at the new renovation. Where was his goddamn wall? How does a wall disappear overnight? But these questions were left unanswered, and before he could even turn to look at his family, he caught the eyes of Mr. Johnson from across the street.

Mr. Johnson was cradling his newborn baby (from his third wife) close to his chest, eyes wide and mouth agape. As head of the HOA, he had personally never particularly liked the Peterses. They always paid their HOA fees last minute; Little Ricky Peters always pitched his baseballs into the Johnson's yard; the teenage girl, Emilia, was always coming home at odd times of night, and once, both the Johnsons and the Peters had brought mac and cheese to the HOA cookout; not to mention that the Peterses were not from Apalachicola, meaning they spoke funny and weren't like the rest. Mr. Johnson stared at the large white beach house, now looking incomplete with the missing wall. He made a mental note to write his neighbors a letter as soon as he got to work that morning.

◼◼◼◼

Mr. Peters learned very quickly that there is not much one can do in the moment about a missing wall. So he went to work like normal, trying to build condos on land that the town would never allow condos on. And Mrs. Peters also went to work, trying to sell vacations to people who would just end up going to Panama City or Destin. Except there were more whispers around the office than usual and coworkers glared at the Peterses when they walked by. Emilia and Ricky went to school, and kids talked behind their backs and sometimes to their faces.

The family tried to keep everything as normal as possible. When they got home that night, Mrs. Peters started to make dinner, Ricky played outside, trying to hit baseballs into his sister's room through the open wall. Emilia screamed at her brother, and Mr. Peters was on the phone, asking anyone if they could rebuild a wall.

By 10 P.M., the Peters were all crowded in Emilia's room, staring harshly at the missing wall, or rather, staring straight into their front yard. They were all hoping that the wall had been there all along. However, no matter how hard they looked, the wall never mysteriously popped up, never grew out of the floor, and never magically appeared when the family rubbed their eyes.

Finally, Mr. Peters, who was never one for wasting time, announced that he was going to bed, and after ten minutes, Mrs. Peters followed him. The children each went to their rooms, with Emilia in the guest bedroom.

▓▓

The next morning, Mr. Peters woke up to a woman calling his name. He cracked open his sleepy eyes and standing outside of his room in their robes and bare feet on the grass were the Watsons. They were pulling their sleeves over their hands and gently rocking back and forth, staring at the Peters's room from floor to ceiling.

Mr. Peters sat upright immediately, shaking his wife's shoulders.

"I think you're missing another wall, Mr. Peters," Mrs. Watson announced, her eyes flickering from the floor to the ceiling and back to the Peters. Her husband said nothing, his mouth hanging open.

But Mr. Peters had already noticed that his bedroom wall was missing. He had noticed that he could now see his next door neighbor's house and he had noticed the warmth in the room and the sound of the AC struggling to keep up. Outside, the sky was dark and heavy, flashes of lightning erupting within clouds. Mrs. Peters, with her cheeks rosy and hair sticking up at odd angles, was sitting with her head in her hands, shaking quietly.

18

Later that morning, the construction workers came in. They looked around where the missing walls had been and saw no damage to connecting walls. The roof seemed fine and so did the floors. So they had nothing to tell the Peterses other than that it looked as if there had never been walls there at all. This did not sit well with Mr. Peters, who told them that there had in fact been walls there before and that he wanted them back as soon as possible.

The truth is that Mr. Peters wanted the walls back because people were starting to talk. He noticed that more neighbors were going on walks down his street than usual and that they were always standing in their yards, staring.

The workers said it would be another three days before they could get the tools and materials to make new walls fit into old walls. Out of pity, they left the Peters with three waterproof tarps and ten wall tacks.

▦

The next night, Little Ricky had a dream that he was taking a shower. The water was very cold and smelled like rain. Eventually, Little Ricky woke up, finding himself lying in a puddle of water in the center of his bed. He looked around his room, noticing that his drawings on the walls were dripping red, yellow, and green and all of his clothes were in heaping piles, water covering the wooden floor, glistening softly in the light of the sunrise.

Little Ricky felt the rain on his back because it hit his neck hard and at an angle. He closed his eyes and took a deep breath, turning around to see the outside, rather than his fourth wall. He blinked the rain out of his eyes and noticed six-year-old Maria Hanner and her parents staring at him from the window of their own house. Their mouths hung wide open and finally, Mr. Hanner walked forward and snapped the blinds shut.

The sound of heavy footsteps marching up the stairs rung in Little Ricky's ears.

"Little Ricky! Emilia! There's another goddamn wall missing in the goddamn kitchen and then one of you took down all of the tarps! I swear to God when I find out who did it, I'm gonna-" Mr. Peters walked into Little Ricky's room and stopped mid-sentence, surveying the fourth missing wall. After a while, he gently closed his eyes and took a deep breath, turning around on his heel and walking back down the stairs.

▓▓▓▓

Downstairs, Little Ricky and Emilia found that the kitchen wall was missing as well. The rainstorm had destroyed the Peters's refrigerator, their dishwasher, their microwave, and everything on the counter, including Mrs. Peters's laptop. The floor was covered in water, soaking through the Peters's socks.

The TV blared in the background with a weatherman dancing across the screen, pointing to the green eye of a hurricane. "We are now under a state of emergency. Everyone evacuate to either higher ground or further inland, and never drive your car into a flooded area…" said the weatherman with slicked-back hair and a blue suit.

The tarps, given to the family by the construction workers, had inexplicably disappeared. Previously, Mr. Peters himself had tacked the coverings to the corners of where the missing walls had been. Now, the missing walls demanded to be seen.

▓▓▓▓

That night, Mrs. Peters begged for her family to all sleep in the living room with her. She felt butterflies in her stomach all the time now and she almost swore that her hair had turned a little grayer over the course of the week. What if she said goodnight to her children and suddenly the floor fell out from under them? What if Emilia started sleepwalking again, right out of her missing bedroom wall?

Therefore, Mrs. Peters found peace only in watching her kids all night while they slept in the living room. Emilia was sprawled on the couch, Little Ricky was on the floor, and Mr. Peters slept on the

20

recliner, which his wife knew would make him feel horrible in the morning. But Mrs. Peters was extremely tired herself and no matter how fiercely she fought the drooping of her eyelids, she, too, eventually fell asleep to the sound of thunder in the distance.

Mr. Johnson was the first to see the Peters's house that morning, or rather, he was first to see that the Peters's house was not there. He even smiled a bit when he saw that all the walls of the house were gone. He could see straight through it and into the backyard, and as Mr. Johnson stood there, he started to laugh. He laughed even harder when it started to rain, thunder and lightning everywhere.

The next neighbors to join Mr. Johnson outside were the Watsons, and they were less than thrilled about the disappearance of the walls of the Peters's house. Mr. Watson even whispered something to his wife about property values going down.

Then, the Hanners were brought outside by their daughter, Maria, who checked on the Peters's house right when she had woken up that morning. She told her parents that it was magic and that she hoped *their* walls would start disappearing soon. Mrs. Hanner scolded her and whispered something to her husband about the corruption of children.

It only took ten more minutes for the rest of the neighborhood to show up. By eight o'clock, dozens of people had gathered around the Peters's house, watching them sleep, blissfully unaware of the crowd gathered around them. The storm was getting stronger, but the neighbors didn't seem to mind. They stood wet and dripping under the dark clouds, an evil glee spread across their faces.

Mrs. Watson cleared her throat and screamed over the thunder. "Mr. Peters! Mr. Peters! You seem to be missing more walls!"

This woke Emilia up and she was so startled that she shook her parents awake and looked frantically around at the mob now surrounding her house. But is it still a house if it doesn't have walls?

Mr. Peters sat up and glared at his neighbors. "What's the meaning of this? Why-" But he could not finish his sentence, because he had noticed the missing walls, the missing house.

Wind and rain howled through the remains of the house. And then everyone started talking at once.

"Mr. Peters, it is against HOA policy for a house to have no walls!"

"You can't even call this a house anymore!"

"I always knew something was up with those Peterses."

"We can't have a house in the neighborhood with no walls!"

"Maybe they're messing with us!"

"Now, I told you months ago that the Peters are weird!"

"They must leave immediately!"

"What about *my* walls? Will *my* walls disappear?"

Mr. Peters sat back into his recliner and grabbed the remote. Emilia laid back down and covered herself in her blanket while her brother snored quietly beside her. Mrs. Peters also leaned back and stared at the TV as Mr. Peters clicked the on-switch.

The TV showed nothing but black and white fuzz, the sound of static and thunder filling the room and drowning out the voices.

HARVEST

ROSALEEN LYNCH

She held the glass jar over his last breath. To be preserved. Sealed with wax paper and wire wound round. She'd already caught his last words on the gramophone. Those she would return to his family. The breath she would keep.

The window shelves were a stained glass of sky, sea and autumn coloured jars. Lids drum-tight and wired shut. Loose lips sink ships, last breaths bring them back. Messages in bottles. Salvage.

The gramophone record was labelled, in its sleeve ready to be broken with bread over the grave. She rinsed out another jar. This time a breakfast marmalade.

APARTMENT SCENE

DAVID CAPPS

You're far from the dancer of the seven veils I chased until noon—

I rise at the pitfalls of your stentorian alarm:

>Sandy!

What is it that strikes my wide-eyed wonder while I awake, and she
in slothful thanks of morning slumbers through the horseful baritone:

>Sandy?!

Voiced as though everything seeks a natural end, yet flies at angles
to the finding

>Sandy!

And she, peaked under the covers, her mouth like a fruit, open and
snoring loud, or she is like

>Sandy!?!

or she is like a slow, slow loris hiding with moonshot eyes
hinter the steely curtain, with pairs of underwear strewn across the
floor
with popcorn and tissue paper and flavor of garage
     Sandy!

What letters come next of eviction, of the hospital where you wear
your blue garbs perpetually late with ease?
     Sandy!

Who is this man who calls you while you stay hidden within our
apartment complex,
on the lower level, in bed beside the curtain

Calling strong, as though you were the missing person on the milk
and he
the mother.

THE SOUND OF A FLINCH

EILEEN CUNNIFFE

If the term "beady-eyed" was not coined in reference to the mourning dove, it ought to have been. I've had ample time to assess the shiny black eyeballs of these pretty birds over the last three summers, since a pair (maybe pairs?) of them determined that a hanging flower basket just outside my back door is the perfect spot for nesting. Again and again. And then once more.

I only ever see one beady eye at a time, because the birds always position themselves parallel to the door, although not always facing the same direction. Seen in profile, I can appreciate their delicately shaped heads and the sharp black beaks that curve downward ever so slightly. I love, love, love the cocoa-powder brown of their feathers, flecked with soft black spots. I love the way they sometimes collapse their heads deep into their bodies as they guard their precious eggs. I even love their plaintive four-note call, the reason the doves are described as "mourning"; I recognized this a distinctive element of my local soundscape long before the birds took up residence in my flower basket, although I've noticed they never sound these notes while nesting.

Here's what I don't love: having a brightly colored flowering plant purchased from my favorite nursery wither and die because I cannot water it while the doves are nesting. Having my back door—the easiest access to my herb garden, my detached garage and my hose and watering can—commandeered for weeks, even months, at a time. Having to dispose of those weeks'/months' worth of accumulated bird droppings and sticky fragments of eggshell at the end of each summer. Having to replace the fiber liner in my wire hanging basket every spring. Never so much as a thank-you note left behind, and no way to withhold an unmade security deposit to cover the damages.

And what I most especially don't love is the way the doves make me flinch—over and over again—sometimes just because I've opened the storm door to let fresh air into the kitchen, other times because I've dared to crack open the screen door and tiptoe down my back steps. *My* back steps.

It's a mutual flinch, I know, and on both sides it's instinctual. We startle each other, almost every time. Typically, it's a six-part movement: the click of the lock on the heavy storm door, the metallic ping of the lock on the wood-framed screen door, the rub of the door against its jamb (especially on steamy summer days) as I gently ease it open. And then, a flash of brown feathers and a low-level squeal as the bird takes flight, accompanied one-half beat later by a half gasp/half shriek from me, and a rocking motion as the basket swings on its hook. I've come to think of this sequence as the sound of a flinch.

Some of what I know about mourning doves I've learned from my mother. The first summer they moved into my flower basket, Mom was recovering—oh-so-slowly—from a series of medical challenges that had kept her in the hospital and then in a rehab facility for nearly six months. I'd tell her about the doves when I'd visit with her, knowing she sorely missed the view of trees and birds from her own kitchen window and felt deprived of her webcam obsession with an eagles' nest and the daily drama of waiting for those far-away eggs to hatch. She's the one who told me that male and female mourning doves take turns minding a nest. She thought it was funny that they startled me so often, and that I resented having my back porch taken over by birds; she would have loved such close viewing and such intimate encounters. As I gave Mom updates and saw her take great pleasure in them, my stance toward the doves softened. By the time those first eggs had been fledged and had morphed into squabs, they'd kind of won me over. I did enjoy watching that little family through the screen door, or more stealthily from my dining room window. I was nearly as proud as the parent birds when those babies flew my coop.

Until I saw what they'd left behind in the ruined basket liner. Yuck. I made a mental note to buy some netting the following spring, to make it clear that my flower basket was not accepting tenants and was not available for use as a birdy birthing center and latrine.

But by fall, when I should have been tucking that basket and others away in my garage, I was preoccupied with the emptying out process of a different nest. Mom's health was improving, but after what she'd been through—and with Dad having developed new health challenges, too—my six siblings and I were preparing to help my parents move out of the house they'd lived in for 55 years, and into an apartment in a nearby senior community. I managed to rake the leaves in my yard, but forgot all about the hanging baskets and so many other tasks I've come to think of as putting my garden to bed for the winter. The nest where we'd all been fledged as young humans needed clearing out and sprucing up—and yes, a bit of mourning—so we could sell it. All my energy was wrapped up in that effort from early fall well into the beginning of the next summer. Through a winter of wicked Nor'easters, I watched snow pile up in the three flower baskets on my back porch. Then, before I even had a chance to think about buying annuals for my garden, or netting for my best hanging basket, the doves had moved back in and were settled comfortably around the skeletal remains of an ornamental pepper I'd planted at the end of the previous summer. A new season of nesting and flinching and fledging and making a filthy mess was well underway.

Gentle reader, this feels like the right moment to let you know that since I moved into my house 18 summers ago, I have always had bird houses scattered around my property. They've hung from the tree in my front yard, perched beneath my living room window, dangled from the back fence, and swayed from poles placed among the shrubbery. I'm always thrilled to see twigs poking out from the openings of these small abodes or to observe motion that lets me know someone has accepted my invitation to move in. I thrill at the birdsong that greets me every morning beginning in early spring, I mourn its lapse during the colder months. I hope you will keep this in mind when I tell you that after two years of having my back porch commandeered and the floral selections for my favorite basket ruined, I decided this spring to make it clear to the mourning doves that they should find somewhere else to nest. I bought a pretty purple plant for my hanging basket. Then I took the remnants of a broken old windchime—one made from mismatched pieces of silverware—and tucked those pointy objects around the outer edge of the flowers. It was a not-so-subtle sign that clearly read "Keep Out." And it worked. Or so I thought. Until the final weekend in July, when in the throes of a nasty heatwave, I noticed some twiggy debris on my back porch as I approached the steps. Then suddenly, a tawny flash, that odd little squeal, and me, caught off guard, once again emitting my own half shriek/half gasp. The sound of a flinch, when I had at last stopped expecting it.

So we are now in our third season of scaring the feathers off each other on an almost daily basis, me and my mourning doves. I am intrigued by their ability to take off and land around the pointy utensils in the nest, although I've noticed the fork closest to my door has been nudged into a new position. I don't dare reach into the nest to remove the utensils now for fear of further aggravating the situation. Mom is oh-so-happy to hear that the mourning doves have returned to my flower basket. She's even happier after I tell her what I'd done to try to keep them out. She eagerly awaits news of the soon-to-be hatchlings.

I have no way of knowing if it's the same pair of doves nesting in my basket every time, but in addition to what has Mom told me, I've done a little research. I've learned these birds like to nest under eaves or in other partially sheltered spots, and that once they find a nesting place they like, they are inclined to return, as many as five times in a single mating season. Each time they nest—typically with two eggs—the male and female take turns incubating, just as Mom explained; for about two weeks, he takes the day shift, she takes the night shift, with one or the other constantly on duty. I've never seen the changing of the guard, but the birds are so similar in size it appears as though the same creature sits in stony silence all day and all night—except, of course, when I get too close and s/he hits the ejector button and temporarily flashes off to the peak of my garage roof, where I swear s/he gives me a beady-eyed dirty look.

Once the eggs hatch, the mama and papa continue to share parenting duties for another two weeks or so as their fledglings develop. Those are the weeks I don't even think about using my back steps, because the adult birds are on red alert against intruders. Why, I wonder, can these birds remember exactly which house and exactly which hanging basket to nest in, but look at me every time—through that one unflinching glassy black bead—as if I am a brand-new threat, not an accommodating (if reluctant) landlady? Why can't they just let me slide past the nest, walk down three steps, take out the trash or collect a handful of basil from the garden, then slip back through the door without getting their feathers ruffled? Don't they see how I check on them after every thunderstorm, or how I shooed those big, noisy crows out of the yard just the other day?

I read online recently that what I've thought of as a squeal—the sound of a mourning dove launching into flight (from anywhere, not just from my hanging basket full of dead flowers and patinaed eating utensils)—is a sound made by the bird's wings, not a gasp of surprise from its breast like mine, which is how it always strikes me. In its own way, this new information startles me, making me feel more skittish than the birds. The sound made by their wings has been described as "a sharp whistling or whinnying." But to me, it's the sound of a flinch.

BORDER TOWN

JOHANNA DEMAY

Ciudad Juárez & El Paso simmer
in a brew spiced with sibling rivalry
and desert heat. Country crooners
and *mariachi* bands arm-wrestle
for sovereignty over the airwaves,
sing siren songs to lure one another
across the line.

They sway to each other's rhythms,
swallow each other's words.
La riata becomes "lariat."
"Green grow the lilacs"
morphs into *gringos,* blue eyed
foreigners with pink skin
and straw colored hair.

In Juarez a sixth grade teacher
lectures on the 1910 Revolution.
Fingers drumming the desktop, his star student
dreams of climbing the fence beside I-10,
thumbing a ride to LA. A neighborhood
pusher loiters outside, baggies stuffed
in front pockets, pistol stashed behind.

On a day-trip I stop at an outdoor café.
An old street singer serenades me,
hands calloused, fingernails
blackened, cracked guitar weathered
as a cheap kitchen chair
left too long in the sun.
But it still makes music.

Church bells chime, loudspeakers bray,
teenagers head-butt soccer balls.
In tin cans nailed to adobe walls, geraniums
bloom hope-bright. A two thousand mile-long
jagged wound, numbed with narcotics, sutured
with steel mesh and barbed wire, the border festers.

BLAMING JUSTIN BIEBER

DEAN GESSIE

His uncle woke him up with a boozy, baritone rendition of "King of the Road". Something or someone was *for sale or rent* and the speaker *ain't got no cigarettes*. Uncle Jack was on the dole because he had a bad back, a drinking problem and unpredictable employment as a bush pilot. When the cheques came out, he and Jim Beam took a seat at the kitchen table and regaled Stephen's father who, given opportunity, imbibed like a mosquito on a moose, *to be social*, he would tell Stephen's mom. It was difficult to square Uncle Jack's reputation as a gap-toothed *bon vivant* with two divorces and a kid in juvie. But Uncle Jack liked to wax sage in the form of questions, *Can't we all just get along*? To Stephen, this seemed sensible, but the devil was in the details.

Stephen would *get along* if it meant saving his venom for a closer target. He peeked through the cloth curtain separating his bed from the tiny living space that abutted the smaller kitchen. He studied the droopy-eyed self-absorption of his father. His dad's hands appeared to be made of Velcro or fly paper. They stuck to the bottle and his own shot glass. More infuriating was his dad's pubescent cackle. It was like listening to a hyena vocalize glee before a ripped purse of steaming guts. Stephen tried to cotton his ears with his pillow. Nothing worked. It was a long night of penance for sins Stephen could not recount much less imagine.

But no repast is complete without dessert. Stephen awoke much later to the sight of his naked father stumbling toward the chamber pot. He was riding the arm of Stephen's mom, Gail. Their own bed was a stone's throw away and only separated from his by another of the ubiquitous curtains. Stephen often wondered why their cottage remained in the Dark Ages while all the others had air conditioning, satellite dishes and actual running water. In any event, the theatre was bad, very bad. Stephen watched, cringed and boiled as his dad pissed all over the floor, the wall and the oil stove and his mom, pot in hand, tried to field the stream like a gold-glover.

"Jesus, Frank," she said. "Watch what you're doing!"

When he awoke for the hundredth time, he smelled immediately the industry of his mom and his Aunt Jane. He crawled to the bottom of his bed and peeked through the curtain. They were shuffling around the linoleum in the kitchen filling countertops with rows of partially cooked cabbage, steamed rice and hamburger. Tomato sauce was bubbling on the wood stove. Elsewhere, on the kitchen table, there were baskets of beets, string beans and onions. After the making of holubtsi, borscht was in the docket. Later, as per tradition, they would bring out blueberries and raspberries and make pie.

Stephen's dad was there, too. He was in his work clothes sitting quietly on the sofa, his back to the picture window overlooking the lake. When a car horn sounded outside, he rose unsteadily and proceeded toward the door. He hovered around his wife for a parting kiss, but he never got one. He was only seconds out the door when Stephen's mom developed a text she had apparently started already.

"I could kill him," she said. "He knows he can't handle liquor but he likes to pretend he can. And Jack!"

Aunt Jane punctuated her remarks by stuffing cabbage leaves with red meat. She didn't look up. "Everything's about *being a man* with

35

them. They have no shame! In fact, Ted got into the shower with me the other day -"

Stephen recoiled in his bed. He had a vague idea that the conversation was going to be embarrassing forthwith. It angered him to no end that adults mistook curtains for walls. He dressed quickly and appeared. "Where's dad going?" he said.

"He got called into work. There was a storm in the city last night. Power's out." His mom looked at Barb. "Serves him right. He'll suffer."

Aunt Jane suggested *tit for tat*, that ice water Gail *tie one on* herself. She elevated a Walmart bag with two bottles of wine in it. Aunt Jane said that Gail had already *punched her card*, that she would be *in that number, when the saints go marching in.*

Stephen didn't listen. He went out back to what was euphemistically called *the shack,* a storage shed repurposed as a bedroom. His older brothers had bunked there during earlier summer vacations, created wallpaper of nude female pin-ups. Between Gail and her eldest, the choice of decor had been a knock-down-drag-out battle and she immediately removed the pictures when Drew and Michael started to stay home summers to work. All that remained were ghostly white rectangles, reminders of old wounds unbandaged. Sometimes, for Stephen, the rectangles were windows upon deep feelings of shame.

Now, one of two beds in the shack had been replaced with a small desk and a bookshelf. Stephen was already reading teenager tomes like *The Maze Runner* and *Life of a Loser*. Today, in honor of her birthday, he was recopying a freshly written poem for a girl he loved whose name he did not know. He remembers the introduction.

"Look!" her mom said, "our son has a new little friend!"

Stephen was the *new little friend* of Muthusamy or Sammy, a boy of the same age who was quite small and precocious. "Stephen," said Sammy's mother, "this is my daughter, Kamalarani."

He was smitten immediately. All the world's butterflies shimmied in his stomach. But it was hard to court someone whose name you couldn't remember and Stephen was too embarrassed to ask her or her brother to repeat it.

The Mahadhevan family were Tamils originally from Sri Lanka. When the retired school principal died three doors down, the Mahadhevans bought the cottage as a summer retreat from Portland. Stephen's dad said, "The Tamils from Sri Lanka speak English better than we do." Stephen's mom said, "The Tamils from Sri Lanka seem very nice." They had a Lexus, a speedboat and a fire pit.

Sammy and Stephen did most everything together for the first month of vacation. Frequently, in the large porch at the back of Sammy's cottage, the boys would wrestle in the king-sized, extra bed at one end. Stephen was taller and would pin his smaller opponent. One day, however, he found himself with his head between Sammy's thighs. He told himself he could make Sammy laugh by pursing his lips and blowing hard on Sammy's soft flesh, but his lie to himself and his breathlessness were both obvious. He saw Sammy less often after that because what Sammy knew made Stephen feel uncomfortable.

But, to a point, the fire pit was safe neutral ground. It was lit most nights by Sammy's father and Stephen and the Mahadhevan family enjoyed hotdogs or hamburgers or s'mores. One night, when just the kids were about, Sammy's sister taunted Stephen. She was three years older and she liked to kid him because he was an apostate. She could see idolatry in his eyes.

Sammy's sister held up a s'more sandwich. "What do you think, Stephen? Do you think a Tamil girl and an American boy can be delicious together?"

The question confused Stephen. In the tapered fingers of Sammy's sister, the gooey confection looked like the bobbing head of a cobra.

"Do I have to draw you a map?" Sammy's sister pried open the s'more sandwich ever so slightly. "You can see," she said, smiling wryly, "how the Tamil chocolate and the American marshmallow are in bed together."

The metrics of the joke were old, but Stephen didn't know any better. He leaned back in his chair because his face was burning up in proximity to the fire. Sammy's sister was giggling and Stephen hated how much he loved to look at her and listen to her laugh.

Sammy said, "If you waste a s'more, I'm going to be very upset."

Mostly, though, fire chat was the purview of Sammy's father. He had a shock of grey hair and a fleshy paunch. He liked open dress shirts over printed floral shorts. Sasitharan Mahadhevan loved Dodgers baseball and often listened to the games on the radio around the fire pit. He was a barrister and he talked like one. Unprompted and unannounced, he would get to his feet, breathe deeply of the night air, silence chatter with an index finger to his lips and then list the reasons that he was grateful for American citizenship. His family rolled their eyes, but their smiles were inclusive.

It was a different matter, however, when Sammy's dad had too much to drink. He kept a cooler full of Budweiser beside his lawn chair and made regular withdrawals. On those nights, Sammy's dad would sing patriotic songs of independence, songs that he had learned as one of *the boys* or Pudiyangal. This prompted his wife to claw at her husband from the edge of her chair and to plead in her own language what Stephen understood to mean, "Stop! Sit down!"

Sammy whispered to Stephen with complete detachment and even a shrug, "Maybe my dad was a terrorist. Maybe he wasn't." He extended his arms to either side, elbows bent, hands skyward, like a Shiva yogi. "Who knows?"

Sammy's sister was equally ambivalent. She surfed the air with a cobra s'more.

Stephen rose to his feet and pushed the chair under his desk. He had left the shack and returned many times. Once, he walked through Windy's Lot where the blueberries grew best; another time, he circled

38

the canal landward of the lake lock, tossed pebbles into the shallow water and watched impassively as the suckerfish scattered. Other forays he would not remember. He looked almost entirely inward.

He had re-written the poem dozens of times, adding and subtracting the same words like beads on an abacus. He was frustrated by his lack of progress, the idea that any version of the poem was imperfect. He told himself repeatedly that his were honest feelings and that he needed to find the courage to share them. He was unware of the hubris of his strategy, packaging his feelings as a gift.

Poem in pocket, Stephen was met at the door by Sammy.

Sammy said, "Get in here. You gotta see this weird scene. It's all hell!"

Stephen didn't notice the spinach puttu, string hoppers and vegetable curry on the dining room table. He didn't read on the wall the Christmassy lettering that spelled, *Happy Birthday*. In the length of one breath, he had moved through the main room and into the back porch. Air conditioning made the room feel like cold storage.

The *weird scene* had several parts. Sammy's sister was performing a hip hop dance to a song called "Sorry" by Justin Bieber. At some points, she leapt onto the large, king-sized bed and made whirring scissors of her legs. All the while, her eyes were distant as she mouthed the choreography, *heel, toe, heel, toe, five, six, seven, eight, make a fist.*

Sammy whispered to Stephen that she was *supposed* to do a village folk dance in the costume provided by her parents. "It's a *tradition!*" His eyes popped from his head, communicated competing currents of shock and mockery. "Look at her! Can you believe it?"

Stephen looked at the rumbled blouse and petticoat in the lap of Sammy's mom, the long folds of a sari that fell over either knee like the moulted skin of a garter snake. Sammy's father sat rigid and hidden behind aviator sunglasses.

Stephen's hand reached into his pocket. His fingers closed around his poem as though he were extinguishing the light in his heart. He watched the bare midriff of Sammy's sister as he crumpled the poem into a ball. He heard *jump up, push down, groove, groove* and then play-by-play from a Dodgers matinee. He hadn't heard the radio before.

Sammy's father went to the screened windows fronting the cottage and overlooking the lake. With his shirt sleeve, he wiped his nose and dried his eyes. Outside, the late afternoon sun and heat were oppressive, but he cranked open one of the window panels, looked at and listened to what caught everyone's attention.

Stephen's mom and Aunt Jane were whooping it up in the water, splashing and twirling and churning through the sandbar that inclined to deep water beyond. They had spent all day cooking around the woodstove and, at Jane's insistence, *rehydrating* with wine. Now, they were drunk and they were skinny-dipping and they were, to all appearances, unaware of a community of gawkers or the high afternoon sun.

Stephen was frozen with horror. He felt doubly betrayed by obscenity and abandonment. To make matters worse, Sammy's dad turned from the window and announced to no one in particular, without judgment, what was obvious to all. "Mrs. Olynyk is three sheets to the wind. And she's naked as a jaybird."

He then looked at his wife, as if he were directing traffic at an accident scene, and asked her to get into the small, outboard boat, to go help Mrs. Olynyk and whoever else was with her. "Make sure they're okay," he said. "Stay with them, if you can." He added, "I would do it myself, but -"

Stephen looked at Sammy, his wide eyes and half-open mouth, heard the things that Sammy didn't say, *Look at her! Can you believe it?* It was more, way more than Stephen could bear.

He did not excuse himself. When the screen door behind him recoiled on its hinge and smacked the jamb, he didn't hear it.

He walked rapidly toward home, his eyes fixed on the green grass.

He had the feeling that everything was combustible, that he was made of straw and carrying fire, that he would no longer long for anything anymore and that nothing about this day or any other would ever be good in his memory or dreams.

At the Campbell camp beside his own, he veered diagonally through rocks and brush and almost fell when his ankle turned. He emerged from behind the woodshed, sped by the figure of his father in the driveway, entered the shack and threw himself onto the bed.

His father couldn't hear him crying or guess the reason for his self-absorption. In his hand was a brown paper bag full of marshmallow s'mores.

THE DUPLEX

WILL WELLS

I told my wife there'd been a fire —
two dead from smoke inhalation.
And we knew them both, if knowing
includes a nod and brief banter
across porches or between cars
wedged in the gravel patch that doubled
as driveway and hardscrabble backyard.
We'd nicknamed them the rowdy girls.

They partied late with a parade
of roughneck boyfriends whose 4 X 4's
blocked us in on workday mornings
until our frantic honking roused them,
like auras of their coming hangovers.
We wondered whose bedroom backed

our bedroom wall, but her repertoire
of love cries inspired us to caution.

When one got pregnant and bore a child,
we dropped off a plate of cookies
under Saran Wrap stretched thin as our smiles.
Their ripped screen door sagged from hinges,
one slam shy of complete collapse.
And there we stood, fidgety, at loss
for words, the proper couple who hid
behind Door One, our presence like

reproach, or the reveal of a game show
prize they hadn't won. But who knows?
Perhaps they pitied our deficiency
in reckless joy. Since moving in,
we'd been saving for a starter home,
better neighbors. The month after
Children's Services showed up to remove
the little girl, whose name we never learned,

our home loan closed. We left as soon
as our lease ran out, the month before
their lives ran out. Our vacated rooms
provided space to host the fire set
by a jilted boyfriend, who wept
confessing he had *only meant*

to smoke them out.... Nightmares scorched
our new master bedroom for some weeks...

the ceiling imploding around us
as our curtains, billowed by night
breezes and doubled in the mirror,
fanned flames of panic and stirrings
of remorse. We had lived next door
to joy and tragedy, holding both
at bay. The dead lay past saving.
We wondered what could rescue us.

DOG-EAT-APE WORLD

MIKE BENDZELA

A canid captive since it was a pup had learned to distinguish between the tribeswomen and the tribesmen, and even tribe from tribe. It heeled and cringed in the presence of the hairy woods folk and tore into the flesh of the herbalists. It came down to a matter of smell — these apes all basically tasted the same — and the dog wasn't fooled by this particular ape's pretense of superiority over other apes.

So, when the keeper goaded the dog into attacking an herbalist that had wandered onto tribal territory, and then stood back to observe the ensuing mayhem, shouting, "Good dog!", the canid reminded the ape:

"I am but a proxy for your own savage instincts which, like us dogs, are cultivated and deployed at will."

CUL DE SAC, IN AMBER

DAISY BASSEN

We are the people of houses and trees,
Seventy-year old maples in mown yards.
The elms are all gone. We aren't familiar
With the way the light settles across a meadow,
Ricochets through a city block, tidal with diesel fumes.
Our vistas are modest: the creek sneaking
Below a bridge, the reeds strew with old green
Glass from bottles, an Italian restaurant reflected
Under the swan's path. No one has lived here
Forever like moss loving stone. We know the sound
Of cicadas, the off-year stragglers, the waving neighbors
Who are not our countrymen. The sky is cut
With Blue Angels. We welcome thunderstorms,
A door to largeness, a tribe, the sensate crack
A broth for memory, for dreams of middle-age.

ALEJANDRO

CHRISTINE KINDBERG

The bus ate the curb in two gulps—one wheel, then the other. The back of Alex's head smacked the headrest, then he slammed into the seat in front of him. The bus ground to a stop, and he ricocheted against the seat back hard enough to feel the solid interior under the foam. An orange backpack fell on him from the overhead bin.

Everyone was cursing in their home language: Portuguese, Mandarin, Hindi, English in a variety of accents, and the tour guides in Spanish.

They hadn't hit anything—they were just parked on the sidewalk at a diagonal, left side downhill. The bus driver stood and scanned the mountain road for other cars, muttering. Alex shrugged the backpack into the aisle. One of the hard lumps of someone else's stuff had hit him under his shoulder blade. His iPad and his phone had both disappeared, and he had to fish them back by pulling on the white charging cords.

Marianne didn't look hurt, just a little scared: she was craning to see the front of the bus and pulling down the sides of that ugly slouchy hat that covered as much of her hair as possible. It made her look like a white, blonde Rastafarian. She'd made it herself last winter, knitting while reading for her AP English class. Their mom hated it, but Marianne had packed the thing anyway. Alex was with their mom on this. If Marianne went off to college wearing the hat as much as she wore it this summer, people would think she was a skater or a pothead.

Next to Marianne, Sonja was picking up colored markers that had fallen into the footwell. Alex saw an inviting band of toffee skin in the gap between Sonja's shirt and the waistband of her jeans.

If he put his hand there, against her lower back, their skin tones would match.

"Is Francisco getting out?" asked Marianne.

Francisco the tour guide was leaning on the driver's seat, bent down toward the driver's open door. The driver shook his head and closed the door, taking a toolbox with him. Francisco lifted and lowered the black ball cap that spelled out *GUÍA* in white letters, then he turned toward the rows of students and scanned the group. He nodded at Alex and smiled at Marianne, but instead of saying anything, he picked up his suit jacket and climbed over the driver's seat and out the driver's door. Through the windshield, Alex saw the bus driver struggling to lift the hood as Francisco pointed over his shoulder. Marianne chewed on her thumbnail, watching them.

The program instructor was on his cell phone, his voice getting louder with every word until he was standing in the aisle yelling. The Spanish was too fast for Alex. He nudged Marianne.

She barely blinked. "Something about how they promised this wouldn't happen again and they'd better have another bus ready to come pick us up right now."

"You can understand that?" Sonja's Indian accent was more pronounced in the up-turn of her questions.

Alex looped his arm around the headrest. "I told you she's practically fluent."

Marianne gave him a look—no flirting with Sonja. She was like that with all her friends. "You'd be fluent too if you practiced." She flicked his forearm until he moved it back to his side of the seat.

"See what I have to put up with?" He didn't quite look Sonja in the eyes. "I could be sailing at the lake house right now." He shifted to the window seat and leaned his head against the glass, cool against the crown of his head. "If our parents hadn't picked such a good bribe..."

"I told you you didn't have to..."

"They bribed you into coming? What with?" Sonja looked at him. All it would take would be a little smile to get her flirting.

Marianne shook her head. "He whined like a baby. I don't get what the big deal is. You survived it last time we were here."

"You've been to Peru before? Why didn't you say? You could be our tour guides, along with Francisco."

Alex turned to look out the window. Let Marianne answer that.

"It was like ten years ago—we were just kids. We came as a family to see where Alex was born."

"Alex?" Sonja was smiling again. "You mean *Alejandro*?"

During the first roll call two days ago, he'd asked to be called *Alexander*, the way he always did. "*No, no,*" the program instructor had said, one light brown finger pointing to the painted ceiling of the hotel lobby. "*Aquí solamente hablamos es-pa-ñol.*" His finger had marked each syllable like he was trying to get the attention of an orchestra.

The instructor's bio on the brochure said he taught Spanish at three different colleges in Chicago and ran this study travel program in Peru during the summer. Alex had read the brochure just to point out how janky the program sounded. That had only made his parents more convinced he should go too.

"Where are we anyway?" asked Sonja.

The town around them was so small you'd have to zoom way in to see it on a map. Buildings with flaking paint lined either side of the empty highway. To their left, a handful of streets ran downhill, carrying houses with patchwork-metal roofs. Beyond that, the mountains spread out in every direction using the greens of spinach, avocado, and ivy. The afternoon sun glinted off some whitecaps in the distance.

Marianne took one of Sonja's markers and drew a cross-eyed clown on the back of a vocabulary card. "Let's play hangman."

Even without looking, Alex knew Marianne was drawing three-dimensional gallows with steps leading up to the platform and realistic shadows stretching out beside it. When they were kids, neither Alex nor their younger sister could ever convince Marianne to start a game before every little piece was perfectly arranged. Now she was explaining the game to Sonja with too much detail, gesturing with the marker as she talked.

"I'll guess Ñ," said Sonja.

"Hold on, I'm not ready yet."

▓▓▓▓

On the street outside, people were gathering to stare at the bus. They stared openly, pointing with their chins as they talked. They probably couldn't see through the tinted windows, but Alex leaned away from the glass just in case. He felt like he was on the wrong side of the bars at the zoo.

Stray chickens, goats, and even a bedraggled horse wandered freely on the street, between and around the people. The women looked like they'd stepped out of a *National Geographic* photo: brightly colored shawls and full skirts. Everyone was shorter and darker skinned than people had been in the capital.

A Chinese kid a few rows in front of Alex pointed at the window, and students gathered to take pictures of the people on the street.

50

Those outside covered their laughter with stubby hands. One girl waved at the bus.

A dozen boys in what looked like school uniforms chased a soccer ball into the street, then stopped when they saw the bus. Alex saw that their eyes were the same shape as his, and they had his own straight hair sticking up at weird angles. Those boys looked as much like him as his cousins looked like his sisters.

Alex leaned back to get Marianne's attention, but he stopped before reaching her. Would she understand what he meant? One of the boys kicked the ball down the street, and the group was gone as quickly as they'd appeared. Alex stared after them. He wondered if they hated school as much as he did.

The program instructor, still on his cell phone, moved to the front of the bus. The main door of the bus creaked and then hissed as it opened. The instructor walked off without looking back, holding the phone in front of his face so he could yell in it more directly.

Cool air blew down the aisle of the bus through the open door. The instructor disappeared into one of the dusty buildings with advertisements in the windows.

The bus was still for a moment, like a kid who's been handed his mom's wallet.

Then the taller of the British boys stood up from the back row. "It smells like piss in here. I'm out, mates." He pushed his way down the aisle and out the door. The two other Brits and the guy from UC San Diego followed him. They crossed the street toward where the people had been gathered, and then they walked away down one of the cobblestone side streets.

After roll call the first day, the tall Brit had started singing Lady Gaga's "Alejandro, Alejandro, Ale-Alejandro…" every time Alex walked by. He was already in college, like most of the other students, all of them older than Alex and Marianne.

"They just left?" asked Sonja.

Marianne clicked a marker shut. "They're idiots. We'll be ready to go in just a few minutes, and we'll have to wait for them to come back." She stood, craning to see over the raised hood that covered most of the windshield.

She was so obvious. Alex squiggled his eyebrows at her. "Expecting *Panchito* to fix everything?"

Marianne made a face at him. In Lima, Francisco had shown them a bar with live music that wasn't terrible. He'd just graduated from the national university with a degree in marketing, and he was doing these tours as a side gig. They'd run into one of Francisco's cousins on the street outside the bar, and the cousin called the tour guide *Panchito*.

Marianne opened the marker again and turned to Sonja. "Okay, I'm ready to play."

░░░░

Alex had always known he was adopted. People were always asking, even strangers, and his parents were always open about it. There was no hiding it: his mom was blonde and blue eyed, his dad was just as pale, and his sisters looked just like them. Alex and Marianne were just four months apart. Marianne liked to pretend they were improbable twins.

Their parents had encouraged Alex to embrace his birth heritage. But on their trip to Peru when Alex was nine, the drive from the airport to the hotel had taken them through streets that were dirty, crammed with rusted cars, and wailing with sirens and horns. In the dim-lit hotel lobby, he'd seen that the front desk staff was as pale as his mom's Starbucks iced mocha. The server at the restaurant had hazel eyes. That whole week, everyone smiled when they saw his family—and then they'd spot him. Their smiles would waver with questions they didn't voice, and their eyes kept returning to him when they thought no one was looking. Marianne had loved every minute of the trip. He had begged to be allowed to stay in the hotel room to watch Cartoon Network.

52

If he ever thought about his birth mother, Alex unconsciously imagined her according to an illustration from his childhood encyclopedia set. When he was little, a babysitter had once pointed to the Quechua woman and said she was Peruvian, like him. Alex had memorized her broad face, thick dark braids, stoic expression, and colorful hatband on a white, short-brimmed hat. A baby peeked over her shoulder from inside the brightly woven blanket tied across her upper chest.

The blanket's knot was secured with a long, sharp straight pin, and the encyclopedia explained the pin could double as a stabbing blade, if the need arose. Alex had fixated on that pin, worrying that it would hurt her if she moved or bent down. He had been sure that the weight of a baby must have made the pin dig into her skin unbearably. Wouldn't that be enough to make her want to slide the pin out of the knot?

▓▓▓

"I've got a word." Justin leaned over the seats behind Marianne and Sonja, reaching for their game sheet. He was the loner of the program, the one who always stood on the edge of conversations, listening but rarely saying anything.

Sonja handed Justin the paper, and he drew nine blanks right away. "This is the only Spanish word I know..." From his smirk, Alex knew it wasn't something Justin had learned from a textbook. The girls filled in the letters with only three wrong guesses.

"*Hijoeputa.*" Justin announced it like he'd invented the word.

"What does it mean?" asked Sonja.

"It means *beloved family member.*" Justin chortled harder.

"No, it doesn't," said Marianne. "And it's not spelled that way. It should be three words."

"What does it mean?" Sonja asked again.

"Never mind." Marianne turned toward the front and crossed her arms. Her frown looked just like their mother's when she heard "dirty" words in a movie.

Alex hooked his arm around the headrest. Sophomore year, when he'd hung out with Carlos and gotten a lot of detentions, before his mom made him take up swimming, Carlos's nickname for him had been *güerito*—whitey. Alex had tested out a lot of words to throw back at him until he'd finally found a term that had stuck. "*Hijo de puta* means *son of a bitch*."

"Oh. How useful." Sonja took the paper back from Justin and put it at the bottom of the stack. She drew more blanks to start on a new word.

▦

Marianne said she was hungry and started digging through the native bag Alex had told her not to buy at the *artesanía* market in Lima. She could never find anything in bags like that.

"I'm sure the shops would have something." Sonja looked to Alex expectantly. Her smile showed off the curve of her cheeks and her long eyelashes. Alex smiled back.

"Get off the bus? We can't." Marianne looked out the window and tucked a strand of hair back under her hat. She could be a real pain in the ass when she was hungry.

Sonja pointed. "It's just there and back. What's the worst that could happen? We can't get in trouble if the director isn't even here."

Marianne looked at Alex.

It did smell like piss on the bus. "Let's go," he said. "If they get mad, just say you had to buy girl stuff from the store."

▦

But when they stepped onto the sidewalk, Francisco moved to block their way. He smiled at Marianne. "Please will you stay on the bus? There is no need of worry. Our driver is experienced at repairs. We

54

will be in the route in only few minutes." He motioned Alex back toward the bus steps. "Alejandro, this way, thank you."

"It's Alexander." Alex stepped around him. "We'll be right back."

Marianne muttered an apology in Spanish, but she followed Alex and Sonja.

They crossed the street, and Sonja glanced back. "He keeps looking over his shoulder like he's expecting to get kidnapped."

Marianne smiled. "I'm sure he's hoping for a tow truck."

※※

The town was much bigger than Alex had realized from the bus. The air was noticeably fresher and thinner than it had been in Lima—the altitude stole Alex's breath sooner than usual. Everything was concrete, faded paint, and dirt.

Sonja led them past a house with an open window, and the smell of roasted meat and rice teased them. The street turned slightly and opened up to a central plaza, a miniature version of Lima's open square and church. Similar birds fluttered around to peck at crumbs, and similar-looking pushcart vendors were selling fruit, roasted corn, and cheap candy. The vendors only had brands Alex didn't recognize.

"How do you say, *I want this one*?" Sonja pointed to a package of cookies beyond her reach. She was the only person in the tour group who spoke even less Spanish than Alex.

Marianne settled with the vendor, and Alex stretched to crack his neck. That hadn't been so terrible, had it? They could go back to the bus now and the director wouldn't even know they'd been gone. A little side excursion.

A guy about his age, standing in the doorway of a corner store, scanned Marianne and Sonja until he saw Alex watching him. A man rode by on a bicycle with two children, one propped up behind and the other perched in front of him. An old man with a worn-out horse passed them in the opposite direction.

A flash of bright blue caught Alex's eye. A woman's sweater. Her hat was white and short-brimmed, and the hatband matched the hem of her wide skirt, both woven in a pattern of pink, yellow, white, and green. A blanket shawl was wrapped around her shoulders, and a baby with stick-up hair peeked out. An oversized safety pin held together the knot of the blanket baby carrier.

She was talking to a man in sharply pressed pants, at the corner by the church steps. Alex was sure the man would offer to carry the two bulky plastic bags she had in either hand, but instead the man laughed at her, a mean laugh, and spat at the ground. The woman looked down, like she'd expected that, and then turned away. The baby squirmed around in the carrier to watch the man pick his teeth on the street corner.

Marianne was opening her chips. Sonja was waving at the British guys across the plaza with the same smile she'd given Alex on the bus.

The baby started to cry, and the woman reached back to pat his dangling leg. She patted him in rhythm, like she was marking the beat of a lullaby—except the rhythm was too fast, hectic, not soothing at all. The woman turned down a side street.

In a minute, they would be out of sight.

"*¿Adónde vas, Alejandro?*" Marianne liked to pretend she could blend in if she spoke Spanish.

"Nowhere—stay here." He crossed the street in time to see the woman and the baby turn left at the next corner. This street was narrower. The shadows were a relief from the sharpness of the high-altitude sun.

Was it a lullaby that she was singing? He could only hear the shouts of some kids playing tag.

"What're you looking for?" Marianne was following him.

"I just want to see something. I'll be back in a minute."

But when he reached the corner, the woman and the baby weren't there. They couldn't have gone far. The bags she was carrying looked heavy—and the baby too. Was the baby still crying?

If she'd gone through one of the gates to the houses on either side, surely he'd have seen her before she made it inside. Just in case, he checked the windows of each house as he walked by. He saw bright flashes of color from TVs, some framed pictures, a few children running, two men arguing. No sign of the woman. Where had she gone? At the next corner, he looked both ways, but the streets were empty. Had she been asking for money—or help? He turned right this time.

"You're going to get us lost." Marianne was only a few steps behind him.

"Don't follow me. I'll be back in a minute."

"Sure, I should just let you wander around an unknown town in the middle of Peru all by yourself."

The pace of the woman's hand against the baby's leg had been so quick, almost frantic, like a chronometer gone off kilter. The baby was strapped to her back, with nowhere to go. If she were to trip, the baby would go down too.

On this street, only a few houses had gates, and they were rusting off their hinges. A dirt path formed an alley to another street, and he saw a bit of bright blue disappear around the corner at the other end.

Alex hurried. Each breath felt like knives. How could anyone live in this altitude?

"Alex, stop—you're scaring me." Marianne's tone was the same as when she'd tagged along into the woods behind their neighbor's house where he and his friends were playing. She'd begged him to slow down, and then she tripped on a root and bloodied her mouth with a knocked-out tooth. Alex had to walk her back. He'd missed the whole afternoon of play time with his friends.

He stepped around chickens and trash—an old oil drum, a milk crate, a disintegrating diaper. At the other end of the alley, he saw that the street ahead branched into two. A sharp incline blocked his view down both streets. A dog guarded the top of one of them. Alex chose the other one. But when he reached the top of the hill, there was only an empty street with a few little kids and more chickens. Maybe the woman and the baby had taken the street with the dog.

"Alex, come on. What're you looking for?" Marianne had their mother's worried voice when she was trying not to show how worried she was.

The other street was empty too. There was no sign of a blue sweater anywhere. No blanket baby carrier, no baby crying, no song sung so softly only the baby could hear. He'd lost her.

Alex bent over and put his hands on his knees. Each in-breath was shaky. This damn altitude. Damn bus problems. Damn *Peru*. Why had he ever come back?

The woman was just a stranger with a baby. Even if he'd caught up to her, what would he have said? He didn't know enough Spanish to say anything. Even if she'd understood English, he didn't know what he'd say. He'd just wanted to make sure she was okay.

He waited a long time for his breath to steady. When he stood, Marianne was facing him, staring past him with her mouth set like a brick wall. She didn't say anything, just pulled her hat down over her ears.

▓▓▓

They retraced their steps, but when they emerged from the alley, the other street didn't look the same. At the next intersection, Alex couldn't remember which direction they were supposed to take. His phone didn't have reception, and Marianne had left hers on the bus.

They turned left.

After looking up and down a dozen streets, there was still no sign of the plaza or the bus.

Marianne shook her head. "I can just see the headlines. 'Two Americans Disappear from Study-Travel Group. Presumed Kidnapped.'"

"'Siblings Marianne and Alexander Seeley have gone missing in the mountains of Peru. Their own stupidity suspected. Parents distraught.'"

Marianne half-turned his direction. "Why do you tell people to call you Alexander?"

In elementary and middle school, teachers and other students took their cues from Marianne and called him *Alex*. They hadn't had many classes together in high school, but several of the other students already knew him. Now that they were going to different colleges, no one would know his real name unless he chose to tell them.

"I mean, do you really hate *Alejandro* that much? It fits so well here."

What did he have to do with the name on his birth certificate, with the back-of-the-throat *j* that had a hint of Arabic, the rounded *a* that was nothing like their father's nasalized Chicago vowel, the hard *d,* and the half-rolled *r*? It made him feel foreign to himself.

"Why should I go by something I can't pronounce?"

"You never tried to learn how…"

Alex kicked a loose stone and sent it skittering down the street ahead of them. Their parents had hired Spanish tutors, but only Marianne had paid attention. "Why should I have to learn how to pronounce it? Mom and Dad can't."

There were several stores ahead, but no sign of the plaza. The shadows were a lot longer than they had been before.

59

"Why don't you ask someone where the bus is?" Marianne pointed at the stores.

"You ask."

"Why do I always have to do everything? When we were little it was 'Marianne, go help Mom set the table.' 'Marianne, go get me a cup of water.'"

"Yeah right—you're making that up. People talk more easily to a girl."

"Whatever..." Marianne pulled her hat down again over her ears.

※

When Marianne asked for directions, the store owner just looked from her to Alex without saying anything.

Two other people in the store were also staring at them. Alex felt them studying his ripped skinny jeans, his white Vans, his high school hoodie. At least Marianne's hair was still under that damn hat. When her hair was showing, people sometimes crossed the street to touch the shiny blondeness.

"*¿La carretera?*" Marianne rolled her r's perfectly, asking for the highway. Still no response.

One of the men in the aisle whispered something to the person next to him. They both snickered.

"*Estamos perdidos. ¿Nos pueden ayudar?*"

Alex yanked on her arm, but it was too late—she'd already announced that they were lost. He could imagine what potential kidnappers would say: those kids were practically asking for it.

The two people in the aisle stepped closer when Marianne asked Alex what they should do. Alex glared at them and pulled Marianne toward the door.

Before they got to the street, the store owner cleared his throat and pointed over their heads with his chin. "*La carretera está pa' allá,*" he said. "*Recto pa' arriba.*"

"*Gracias,*" said Marianne. Alex didn't hoped they didn't notice her sarcasm.

▓▓▓

Outside, it was suddenly dusk.

There were lights in the direction the man had pointed: a strip of streetlights—a finish line—parallel to them at the top of the hill. Between that strip and where they stood, none of the streets were lit, and none seemed to go straight in the direction they needed. Alex finally saw one street, a little ways away, that seemed to be better lit. They headed toward it.

The wind had picked up, and it pushed hard against them, whipping the loose fabric of their clothing and tugging at Marianne's hat. The streets had emptied of kids. Occasional patches of yellow light poured into rectangles on the street from barred house windows. Alex wished he hadn't wandered so far.

Marianne was holding her hat in place with one hand. But when she stumbled on a cobblestone and braced her fall with both hands, a gust of wind sent her hat wheeling across a fence. It was an empty lot, full of jagged darkness.

"I'll get it," said Alex, but Marianne grabbed his arm before he reached the fence.

"Let's just get back," she said. "It doesn't matter. We'll be fine when we get to the bus."

She tucked her hair into the neck of her fleece. It slipped out after only a few steps, and its paleness glowed in the semi-dark.

▓▓▓

The street ahead was a flannel pattern of black, gray, and dark brown, except for one area, where a lot of lights were concentrated. About

61

twenty men lounged in yellow plastic deck chairs around the patio, drinking and laughing loudly. There was the smell of fried food, and Alex suddenly realized he hadn't eaten anything since they'd left the hotel that morning. Marianne poked him in the back, and he kept moving.

As they got closer, there was a fresh round of laughter, louder than before. Above the noise of the patio, a voice called in their direction: "¡*Hola, gringüita!*"

Marianne turned her face away, and more of her hair slipped out from her jacket. The wind caught it, and it unfurled and flapped against her neck like a flag.

Alex knew better than to look at the guy directly—not in a crowd like this—but from the corner of his eye he could see him, sitting in the middle of the patio, legs splayed out, facing the street, hand on the beer bottle next to him. Just some loudmouth eager to impress his friends.

The man called out again. This time he made kissy noises.

The laughter that edged around the patio had the same mixture of curiosity, amusement, and discomfort Alex had felt at that party freshman year, when he was supposedly spending the night at his friend's house, when the seniors had gotten that girl drunk on purpose and led her into the back room and it had ended up in the news the next day. Alex had told himself he didn't know what was happening, had told himself there wasn't anything he could do. What could he do?

Alex nudged Marianne further to the side of the street, closer to the houses. There were maybe thirty feet between them and the edge of light from the patio. After that, they would be out of the spotlight, safe in the dim-lit street.

The calling caught on like wildfire. "¡*Oye, gringüita!*" echoed from all corners of the patio. Marianne pulled the collar of her jacket up around her face, but that seemed to egg the men on further. "¡*Bonita!*

¡Muñeca! ¡Mira ese cabello! Ven, bonita… Solo queremos darte la bienvenida." In the background were whistles, more slurred catcalls, and laughter.

Someone started calling out in English, "Hello! Hello! Hello! How are you? Hello! Hello!" Laughter from all sides of the patio. Twenty feet left.

Someone else shouted out to Alex : "*Oye, hermano, trae la fula y te compro tragos.*"

"How dare they call you *brother*?" said Marianne.

Fifteen feet left. It was only words, Alex told himself.

From the edge of his eye, he saw the splayed-leg guy, the one who'd started it all, stand and step into the street. He was moving to block their way. Suddenly the laughter from the patio faded.

This guy was Alex's age. Shorter than Alex, but solid beneath his rusty-brown t-shirt and grey pants with patches.

Alex drew in his elbows for a fight. Marianne was right behind him. Too close—if Alex was hit, he would fall into her. He took a step forward, a hand back to keep her away.

"*Hola, hermano,*" said the guy. "Hello, *gringüita.*" His shoes had holes at the base of the big toes. There was only a yard and a half of space between him and Alex.

In every other fight he'd ever been in, Alex had been the one to throw the first punch. He waited to be sure a fight was unavoidable, and then tried to end it quickly. Sometimes hitting first worked, sometimes it didn't.

The guy's nose was short and flat. His eyes were blunted from alcohol, but in them Alex saw rage complicated with disdain. Under that, there was some kind of hurt, like he knew he was going to lose no matter what happened. The guy's face was half in shadow, but Alex knew the guy's eyes were the same dark brown as his own.

Whoever stepped forward next would close the distance to an arm length.

Alex planted his feet, tensed. There was a pattern of three moles on the guy's neck beside the crags of his Adam's apple, under the long, patchy hair that ran down from his chin. Alex had three moles in similar pattern—that same contrast of dark brown pellet against burnt-caramel skin—on the front of his right shoulder.

He didn't even see the punch coming, just felt the smash of knuckles against his cheekbone and the side of his jaw. Instinct kicked in—Alex quick-jabbed with his left—he was blind from the howl of pain, disoriented, but his fist sunk into the unguarded flesh of the guy's middle. He followed it with a right jab and connected with the side of a ribcage. He shook his head to clear his vision. His mouth was full of the taste of copper and iron.

The guy lunged into the empty space between him and Alex—his shoulder caught Alex's waist, knocked him back, flat onto the cobblestone. The guy was on top of him, fist back. Alex jerked and rolled out from under him, knees, elbows, fists hitting where they could. The drunk guy smelled like onions and beer. Alex's fist crashed through the guy's nose, and blood bloomed immediately. The guy's hands came up to his face, and he turned his head to the side with a groan. His fingernails were cracked and dirty. Blood dripped onto the cobblestones under his head.

Alex sat back, stood up. The men from the patio were silent. Instead of meeting Alex's gaze, they looked to the side or back to the beers on their tables. Two had come as far as the edge of the street, but now they looked away too.

Marianne stood alone, both hands tightly clutching the strap of her bag over her chest, mouth open, staring at him.

From one of the houses nearby Alex heard the canned laughter of a television soundtrack. The wind was cold, and the night air was so thin each breath cut through him. All that he could see of the mountains was a blacked-out space against the stars. The strip of highway shone further up the hill with the promise of a finish line.

The guy coughed and rolled onto his right side, knees up to his chest, hands still over his face.

Alex spat onto the cobblestones near the guy's feet. "*Hijoeputa*," he said. His pronunciation was perfect, with no trace of foreignness.

Someone on the patio started laughing, louder than the laughter had been before. Others joined in. This time they were laughing at the man lying in the street.

Alex hated them all.

He would have fought them, one and all, if Marianne wasn't standing there. *Hijoeputas*, all of them.

Together he and Marianne crossed the remainder of the lit area. From the corner of his eye he saw two men surround the drunk guy on the cobblestones, help him up.

As soon as they stepped out of the light, Marianne started running toward the highway. Alex followed her, but he was out of breath after only a few steps. When he slipped, he fell and cracked his knees hard against the cobblestones.

He stood up and limped after her. She was too far ahead—he would never catch up.

Then he saw the bus parked on the edge of the road, just ahead. The motor was running, and the right wheels were no longer mounted on the curb. The lights were on inside. Through the windows Alex could see everyone in their seats, asleep or listening to music. The British guys were there, and Sonja. Francisco stood in the aisle facing the program instructor, both gesturing wildly.

Suddenly, Sonja waved through the window. Then Justin was pointing and everyone was waving at them.

Francisco met them in the lit doorway of the bus. "Alejandro! Mariana! Come in, come in! We were much worried! I was on the point of leaving to look for you."

Behind him, the busload of students started shouting the line of the Lady Gaga song: "Alejandro, Alejandro! Ale-Alejandro, Ale-Alejandro…" This time it had a welcoming tone.

Alex started to explain, but Marianne pushed past him. At the top of the steps, she paused and looked back at him and Francisco. She was still clutching the strap of her bag against her chest.

"*Hijoeputa,*" she said distinctly.

Francisco stared after her.

Alex stumbled down the aisle in her wake. The other students were clapping and cheering, but Marianne didn't look up. When she reached their usual rows, she took Alex's seat rather than her place next to Sonja. When Alex came up, she put her bag on the seat next to her.

Everyone was asking where they'd been. Alex shrugged and made a joke about his sense of direction. Everyone else laughed. She said nothing.

Slowly he sat down next to Sonja. His knees hurt like hell, and his head was pounding. Sonja smiled at him, but he no longer felt like flirting. Let her try the British guys—they'd probably smile back.

Marianne put her head against the window and stared out as if she could make everyone else just disappear. When the bus started moving, she gathered her hair and tucked it into the neck of her jacket, then pulled the collar up around her ears.

Later, after everyone else had gone back to their own things, he nudged her, but she pretended to be asleep. It was like she had no words for him, now that she'd seen what he was really like.

※

It was midnight when the bus arrived at their hotel.

The whole way, Alex kept thinking of the woman with the baby, wondering where they slept. He pictured them lying on a floor somewhere, the baby still tied to her back, the large pin still stuck haphazardly through the knot of the blanket.

Really, it was such a small knot, such a fragile safety pin.

TERRITORY

STEPHANIE K. BROWNELL

Will I cease to love
your country when I cease

to love you? Are you
a country or a man?

Are you a motherland?
When you said you would be my

home did you mean hold me or
hold me back? When you are no longer

my home is your country?
A country without me.

SOMEWHERE ON THE NEXT BLOCK

ANN CASAPINI

Somewhere on the next block, behind a pulled-down yellowed shade, eighty-seven year old Mrs. Sandoval lives alone. She had been a black haired, green-eyed Colombian beauty. Her carefully arranged group of smiling dolls and stuffed animals sits against the wall on the back of her pink plastic covered couch. Along the kitchen windowsill, her vintage glass liquor decanters; each one filled with water and drops of food coloring to create orange, yellow and purple light prisms when the sun shines into the room. On every couch cushion, shoeboxes stuffed with postcards, letters and coupons. On every table surface, stacks of articles from faded newspapers and Life magazines to send to her three daughters and son who all live out of state.

Her husband John had Parkinson's and when his arm tremors had gotten bad, she'd begun sleeping in the living room on the recliner. Although her husband died in '92, she still falls asleep there, watching the new TV that sits on top of her old broken set.

The girls' bedroom is now a sewing room full of fabric and jars of buttons -hundreds of buttons- like brightly colored hard candies on display. Her son's room is still decorated with Beatles posters. Plastic milk crates full of his record albums still sit in the corner. Even now his large metal trunk sits in the center of the rug. It's the one he'd brought home twenty years ago, just before he was taken away in handcuffs by Federal agents.

Mrs. Sandoval's Christmas cacti are bursting with red flowers, their long branches drape over the pots' edges like loving arms beckoning her to stay alive at *least* until next May, when her son will finally be freed.

THE FENCE

D. DINA FRIEDMAN

Rosie shouts and bangs on the window. "Watch the fence!"

I tell her to stop because she sounds like a shrew, shouting at these poor people as they pull out of Dr. Singh's driveway. Rose says she doesn't care if they think she's a shrew. "Watch the fence!" She yells again in this grating voice I didn't even know lived inside her. It's like the cancer is taking on its own vocal effect, rattling against what should be the normal occurrence of cars pulling out of driveways. And it's not insignificant that Dr. Singh is an obstetrician whose role is to bring life into the world, so these young mothers should be thinking about life and all its possibilities when they leave here, not about fences.

"You *should* care that you sound like a shrew," I tell her, and I'm wondering what these women see when they look at my wife through the window. Some crazy witch with just a few remnants of hair grown back from the last chemo and those ugly brown spots on her skin, even though I hate myself for thinking these thoughts about my Rosie, whom I still love as much as I did the day we got married. Why won't she put the same attention she puts into the fence into maintaining her health, a decision she hasn't budged on despite our two sessions with Melissa, the social worker, a girl with painted palm

71

trees on her nails who just nodded and said, "Yes, of course," every time Rosie gave some senseless reason for not wanting to take the drug that will save her life. And when I said that I loved Rosie and didn't want her to die, all Melissa did was nod her head again. "Of course you love your wife." So patronizing she was, talking to me as if I were a child instead of old enough to be her grandfather. "That's precious and sweet, but I don't think you're hearing what she has to say."

I thought they weren't supposed to take a position, these social workers, even if it is Rose's decision, because it's her body, not mine, as the social worker kept pointing out. But doesn't almost sixty years of marriage count for something? I wanted to say, *Rosie, if I could throw up for you or feel your pain, I would. But you can't just leave me. Not when there's another option. We're a team, and now it's like you want to give me your resignation letter. I don't accept it; you can't quit!* But I couldn't say any of these things in front of a girl with palm trees on her nails.

"Watch the fence!" Rosie shouts again. From my observation, the woman in the tan mini-van is nowhere near the fence. And what matters so much about this inconsequential object with its diamond-shaped links that separates the doctor's driveway from the thin line of sidewalk along our house, which leads to nowhere except the garbage cans? Why do we even have this fence? The fence was here when we bought the house, back when Karen was a girl, and I imagine it might have been helpful in keeping her from being hit by automobiles gone askew. But would we have even built a fence if this fence hadn't already been standing? Despite the clichéd wisdom of good fences making good neighbors, I doubt we'd have chosen a fence as the best option for our funds.

If I were the fence, I want to ask Rosie, *would you be so watchful and protective of me?* But this is just my narcissism speaking, something the social worker should have noticed if she were smart and knew all human beings are basically in love with themselves, and that our love for others is merely a reflection of that. I still want to write my book about this topic, but lately, I'm not even so sure I'm right about narcissism because I would throw up for Rose.

"Rosie, have some breakfast," I tell her. "You haven't eaten a thing."

"I'm not hungry." She continues to press her face against the window, which is beginning to smear with the trickling rain.

"I'll get you a banana."

"I told you, Vern, I'm not hungry." She bangs on the window again as a van backs bit-by-bit down the birth canal of this far too narrow driveway. Any dent generated in the fence would be clearly unintentional and not necessarily averted by Rose's shouting, but I wonder if perhaps the mirage of this mission might alter her resolve, give her some reason to stay alive, even if that reason can't be me.

I slice a banana and put it on the table. Sometimes Rose will nibble at food if I put it in front of her. But right now she's too concerned with the next car, an aptly named Dodge Intrepid, which is going faster than it should be, angling close to our side of the driveway.

"Watch the fence!" she yells to the heavy woman inside. There's a thin little boy and a baby in the back. The driver's mirror natters against the wire mesh, making a loud nicking sound. Rose opens the window. "Watch it!" she screams again. It's not clear whether the driver can hear her because the car windows are closed, but the vehicle rights itself, leaving space as it continues to back toward the street, out of our line of view.

"They just tapped it," I tell her. "I don't see any problem."

"Go out and check."

"It's raining. I'll check later."

"No, check now so we can ask Dr. Singh who the patient is."

If my wife weren't so sick and if I hadn't resolved to be the too-hard-to-die-on perfect husband, I'd tell her to check the fence herself, because constantly inspecting this inanimate object, my rival for her

73

affection, has become an almost daily annoying occurrence. But I remind myself that Rose's cancer is a challenge to see how selfless I can be. So I go out into the rain, not because I care about the fence, or even care about Rose caring about the fence, but because I'm a narcissistic *shmuck* just like everyone else on the planet.

The steps are slippery, and at the foot of the stoop a puddle has snaked all the way to the house's foundation. I pick up pieces of wet newspaper that have blown into the yard and put them in the garbage can. If Rose weren't watching for me at the window, I could simply stay here for the prescribed amount of time and tell her the job has been completed, but deliberate deception would mean I'd failed my test of faith and devotion, so I follow her orders and march down the doctor's driveway to inspect for damage. The fence looks fine. I wave at Rose and motion her to open the window.

"No dents. I'm going to the grocery store. We need eggs."

"It's raining."

"I'm already cold and wet. It doesn't matter."

Across the street on the other side of the elevated tracks, the air smells like curry. The sidewalks are full of people from other countries—Indians and Pakistanis, Nepalese, Chinese, Koreans. The Jewish deli that used to be here is gone, and so is the regular grocery store. Only the Indian stores are left, and the Korean fruit store, but everything is fresh there and the Korean lady always asks me how Rose is. I don't want to tell her too much of my business, but when we first got back from the hospital, I came here to buy peaches, because Rosie loves peaches, and I told her things weren't so wonderful, so she gave me extra peaches and some pickled cabbage, which she said was good for the immune system. "Kim-chi," she called it. Rose said it smelled like spoiled guts, and it did, but I was glad she ate the peaches. Our grandson took the "kim-chi." He'll eat anything.

I go into the Indian store to buy eggs, passing all the sacks of beans. I know what they are now—lentils, all different colors, and I wonder if having so many colors is a ruse to make people think that a red one is different from a black one and you have to have both. It doesn't matter since I only buy eggs here. I go to the cooler in the back of the store where I think I see the heavy woman who almost hit my fence, and I realize she's not heavy, but pregnant again, very pregnant. She's wearing orange Indian clothes—those fluffy pants and a sari top. The boy is clinging to her arm and screaming the way Karen used to scream, while the baby, a beautiful dark-skinned girl with silky hair, is propped in a stroller gazing intently at everything around her, her dark eyes fastening on my face as if she's trying to figure out my place in her universe. I want to write about babies, too, how they aren't narcissistic because narcissism is a learned trait, a defense you develop when you realize that you don't matter in the world and that the world is bigger than your perception of it.

"She has a beautiful essence," I tell the woman. "Isn't it wonderful, when their souls are still un-tempered, before life bangs into us?" I'm wondering why I'm saying such things to a stranger. Is it because I can't say these things to Rose any more? The fence may as well be in the middle of our kitchen, bisecting the table we sit at all day.

"Thank you." She says the words with an accent and the boy continues to cry, pounding her with his little fists like Karen used to pound at us.

"Shh!" She leans over and scolds the boy in a language I don't recognize. The boy screams louder, and I'm remembering Karen and her tantrums. Always in public places. Always making Rose and me so embarrassed. If we had known Karen would die so early in her life, would we have cared?

I know I should talk to this woman about the fence and tell her what she nearly did, even if she didn't actually do it, and ask her to please be more careful because this fence so important to my Rosie, whom I love so much and would throw up for, but is it right for me to protect the fence for Rosie, buy into this skewed view that challenges the notion of what things in life are really important, a

75

notion that certainly could be examined in general, but a fence? A driveway? If my Rosie is going to die, is this what she wants to focus on for the rest of her life?

So I don't say anything about the fence and the boy continues to cry. I make a quacking duck noise for the baby, who smiles, then laughs, and I'm surprised when the boy also stops screaming and stares at me as if I'm a creature from another planet. Then he laughs, a lovely, bubbly, full-bodied throaty laugh. And as I take the eggs out of the cooler, I realize, even if it won't change a thing for my Rosie, that I figured out what I was meant to do in this moment to make the world a better place.

PRIVACY IN A SMALL TOWN

STEPHEN SCOTT WHITAKER

Ask someone who lives in a small town
to swallow a Ferris wheel and they will
turn over secrets to a happy life.
Privacy? Perhaps summer, winter,
when windows are clapped shut, otherwise
Desires and fears cry out in the air
that flows and waves seaside to bayside
and channels in between. "This is why!
This is why!" parents calliope,
coming down on a son everyone
knows cheats at school and life. His grandfather
shrunk his partner's aces. Why should he
be any different? The old man
who wears blouses, his gray chest hair flowers

over lace and through gold ropes. Who loves

who and how? It is so and so and so
in the carnival open windows make
of crowned streets. Ballygirls with new coats,
mirror-bound strongmen practicing boasts,
blondes vanishing through grandstand windows,
a sour mashed pitchman for late night
money. A rabbit ringer along hedgerows.
Iron jaw work in America's backyard,
we watch, we see we are terrible neighbors.

THIS NEED UNMET

SALLY K. LEHMAN

It wasn't the dead people who became zombies. The dead were already gone. Their bodies had given up, stopped all those lizard-brain-level tasks, and went on to funeral homes and crematoriums, out of misery or pain or old age, despite all the medical researchers and pharmaceutical companies looking for more new ways to keep a body going. To keep a body breathing.

It was wasn't the dead. It was the loved ones who became the zombies.

The loved ones who would sit, stand, wait around the ammonia scented hospital corridors in sterile white rooms. They were the people who would reach out for one another with long, grasping arms, and go in for the comfort. Would draw each other close, draw strangers close, and unthinkingly hug.

Patient Zero of the Zombie Apocalypse was a healthy thirty-seven-year-old whose sister lay dying in the ICU for five weeks. He sat beside her for hours and listened carefully to everything the doctors told him. And he waited. When others came along to wait with him, he was hugged and he hugged back. Arms extending to arms, clasping and grasping and body touching body, with the obligatory kiss on the cheek. Friends, co-workers, the concerned couple from the apartment above his sister's. All reaching toward the man who waited for his sister to finish her dying. People can bring so many germs with them through the world. Grasping arms rarely get sanitized.

After his sister died, Patient Zero was surrounded by the nurses who offered solace for his loss and praised his dedication, and he was hugged. When he went home that night, he infected his wife and children with that longing for arms reaching for other people. The need to pull another human into their body, the need for lips to connect with skin, to find comfort. Soon, the whole family was blindly roaming the street. Reaching.

The neighbors thought it was a kindness at first. A way to share the heartache of loss. Soon, the whole block of Patient Zero's neighborhood was filled with bodies moving toward bodies, arms always reaching, hands clutching, lips coming for faces.

The neighbors could only get so much from each other, so they spread out into adjoining neighborhoods and, eventually, into the town.

Once that first town fell, there was no holding the zombies back. They moved on, pulling and hugging new people into the disease. In the cities, hipster youth who had once eschewed the fad of bodily contact, saw this as a new *meme* and went with it. They hugged each zombie back until all they could do was go for the hug.

Arms floating in front of bodies, they headed into the next city and the next and the next.

They swarmed.

A remote neighbor of Patient Zero traveled to Norway for work. A town councilwoman traveled to Cabo for vacation. Someone who never knew Patient Zero, had never even consoled that first zombie, went to Kiev to see his dying *babushka*. One person, infected by chance encounter, shaking hands with a business acquaintance, sharing a night of romance, meeting old friends, and, *bang*, the world is filled with people grasping at other people.

The zombies were people who had forgotten about the staples of life – eating, working, talking. The Zombie Apocalypse was one big hugfest infecting the world from sea to ocean to forest.

Luckily, I'm one of the more distant people in the world. Never was a hugger or kisser, and it's not like I'm going to start in at this point. Not even when my own sister died. In fact, I envy the dead. They can rest in peace while I have to dodge the people who just want to tell me how sorry they are for my loss.

ROUTE 114

JESSICA LYNNE FURTADO

All horns and whoosh,
and still two trucks
pull up window-to-window
like the wind-licked road
is a 24-hour drive-thru.

There's so much speed,
and hum, and honk, and screech
that you can hardly see
two men laughing at tongue-

in-cheek from across parted
glass, heat of cracked leather
seats. Mirth thundering up
from the throat like a lion

cub learning to say *free*.

A stampede of metal bodies
bolts like an ugly ballet, leads
with lights, and bellow, and boom-
chicka-untz. The men in front

embrace the stillness of a red
eye's glow, bare tobacco-stained
teeth as they howl through smoke
rings. Their palms on the wheel
grip the curled tail of a dirty joke.

FELIX AND THE BODIES

TRAVIS M. KIGER

Felix was a twin. And his brother died before either of them could walk, and before Felix could learn to say his brother's name – Paris.

Davis Kiger, turtle farmer and my great grandfather, had heard that in New Orleans, some families preserved dead bodies after death so that they would look as they had not died at all, but had only been sleeping for some long time. He decided to have his lost infant preserved in this way. He paid to have the child sealed in a coffin with a glass lid. One spring, one Easter week, in fact, Davis took his boy Felix to visit the body– thought to be preserved under glass and concrete. Felix was seventeen at the time. With Davis' help, the cemetery attendant removed the cement slab from atop the concrete housing. Inside was a child, sleeping under glass. Black curly hair. The two men peered into the past as if it were a mirage – all hazy from the heat of the day painting its picture that danced in the box. They were each awed by the ageless child with porcelain skin who looked as if he may stir at any moment and cry out for a rag or nipple or thumb to suck on. They leaned further to look for wrinkles or cracks in the infant's skin, and the attendant warned, Be careful. If you break that glass, he will turn to ash.

This variety of burial was rare in Louisiana, but Paris was not the only one. There was another girl on the island that had been buried in the same manner as Paris. And then someone else died and the family wanted to put the newly deceased in that tomb, so they raised the first girl up. She'd been dead for fifteen years. She had wiry hair that ran down her sides. She wore a necklace, and she had a bracelet and a ring. Her hands were set as if she were praying. The jewelry possibly sparkling with the sun casting a warm glow around the white body, augmenting the already ethereal nature of the scene – a peaceful angelic statue resting in solemnity. One of the girl's brothers said, Open it, I want to see. A crowd crept closer, as they were nosy, too, and wanted to see for themselves. And when they raised the glass up. *Whoosh!* Smoke went up and all that lay there was bones. Her brother took the chain, the ring, and the bracelet off. His sister was no longer there.

These tales of dead and death live in the tongues and eyes of the storytellers of the island. This one man, his sister died while he was fishing in the Gulf. And when he came back seven or eight hours later, the man found a note in his empty two-room house. They were having a funeral, and as so many people were dying at the time, the custom was to have the bodies in the ground before the end of the day. They had the girl in the hole, and they had nails in the coffins back then, and so he said, Please, let me see her one more time. And the old man said, Okay. He went to work opening the coffin. And when he opened it, the man's sister opened her eyes. The girl said, Please, get me some water. The small crowd gasped and applauded and cried. The priest at the site prayed. And he led the others in prayer. They had just witnessed a miracle. And most surely, they had.

It was not long after Felix visited his perfectly preserved dead infant brother that he was sleeping in the Kiger house. He woke to his mother's scream.

Felix felt his way out of bed, into the other room, and to his mother's side. Davis Kiger was a heap on the ground, clutching his breast. Felix turned the turtle farmer over. His mother spat out at him.

Lever sa calebasse!

Felix lifted his father's head, which glowed in his hands as Julienne raised the lamp, and fear worked out of Davis' eyes and hung in the light. That fear stuck Felix dumbly. The skin in Felix's hands felt heavy and tough, and the fear did not make sense.

Davis Kiger was tough on everybody. The Barthelemys knew this better than anyone. The Barthelemys were neighbors of the Kigers, and they played part in an incident involving chickens and a shotgun. In addition to his cucumber garden, turtle farming, and trawling endeavors, Davis was raising some prize hens with blue feet. *Poulet de Bresse*. Bresse Blue. The Frenchman was infatuated with the yard birds, and he counted them every day. One evening, he arrived home after a long day of trawling in the sun, and thought his flock looked light. He counted the hens. Then he recounted the hens. Then he *re*counted the hens. Davis called inside to Julienne, Julienne, did you cook chicken tonight?

No, Davis, we havin specs, his wife called back.

It didn't take a second for Davis to cut his eyes to the Barthelemys and walk on over. He slung open the door without knocking and the Barthelemys were there gathered around their kitchen table. They were eating chicken.

Bonsoir, ya'll eatin chicken, huh?

Yes, sir, Mr. Davis. We havin chicken, tonight, answered Mr. Barthelemy. He did not look up from his plate where a half-eaten leg dug into a small mound of rice.

Where ya'll got dat chicken?

Ah, dat's our chicken, Mr. Barthelemy said, this time eyeing the visitor to gauge his reaction.

Ok, den. Bonsoir, Davis said with his eyes wide and cutting around the room. Davis then walked around the Barthelemy house looking for evidence that chicken had been slaughtered that day. The Barthelemys didn't raise chickens, so if they bought it, they would have purchased it already butchered. He looked in the toolshed behind the house for a bloody ax. He looked through their trash heap by the road for discarded feet and feathers. Davis found no evidence to substantiate his suspicion. He then thought, Where is the least likely place that someone would look for feathers? Davis tramped back to the Turtle Pen for his shotgun before investigating the Barthelemy outhouse. He peered into the hole and saw a dark pool of sludge and shit. Davis lowered his shotgun and fired a single blast into the shit. Shit flew out of the hole and stuck to his face. So did a mess of chicken feathers. Violence flared into his face so you could see it shine like a red light through the all of the shit and feathers. Davis reloaded his double barrel and stumped back to the Barthelemy house in the grit orange dusk. This time, he kicked in the door, pointed the gun, and the Barthelemys jumped and cowered together like a gang of pups in high water for getting in the trash before a long barrel held by a hell-bent sideways Cajun with shit and feathers still stuck to his face around two roving blue eyes of crazy.

Ya'll bunch of motherfuckers! If ya'll need food, ya'll jes need ta fuckin ask! If ya'll touch mah birds again, I'ma fuckin kill all ya'll!

Davis lowered his double barrel and fired both booms into the kitchen table. The Barthelemys were still screaming as he walked away. Julienne, who'd heard the shots, ran out to meet Davis in the yard.

Aucun problème, he said. Dey won't fuck wit our chickens, again.

And now he was on his back on the cold wood bottom of his bedroom. His head limp in his son's hands. His eyes looked less scared. Then they looked nothing at all. Davis took in a deep breath at 3:10 am. And that is when the turtle farmer died.

After a moment, Julienne put a pot of water on the stove and fetched small white candles from the kitchen; Felix arranged the body so that the feet were facing the door, because that is what was done, back then. Julienne, with a bowl of warm water, returned and lit the candles, setting them to the sides of the body. The ritual began and Felix stripped the body of his father naked. He did this reverently, treating it as a relic. This was the source of his life and heritage. This was the body that taught him to speak. This body taught him of righteous discipline. This body had lifetimes of fish pass through its hands. And now this body lay naked and cold.

Julienne knelt beside the bowl and doused the rag into the water and then wiped it along the forehead of her husband's body. She worked slowly and savored the time. She cried. Felix began with the feet and pressed the cloth coarsely into the soles to scrub away all of the work and the black. Knowing that Davis had given him all things into his hands, Felix now took his father's feet into his hands to wash them. It was done before the sun was up.

All of these years later, I still get spooked when I sit with the grave and run my hands over the concrete box painted white sitting on top the ground in Louisiana fashion like a stubborn oak or dilapidated barge clinging to the shore in defiance of course weather and water that wants to run through. The plaque reads DAVIS JOSEPH KIGER 1901 – 1945. I gotta breathe purposefully to rationalize the tomb is not for the Davis Kiger that is my father. This matter of bodies and names and caring for the dead bind the culture of the Bayou to its history. My dad is stuffed under that box of concrete and old wood and earth, surely. And so am I. And so is Felix with his sweat and humble hands washing his father's cold feet in the lamplight. L'histoires – the stories – work as thread stitching the fabrics of years of disconnect and generational gaps into patterns of family and home in the way that chapters add up to a complicated novel that makes little sense if read every other chapter at a time. How can anyone know where they came from without knowing how they've cared for their dead, and their names, and everything in between? How can anyone know anything without knowing how a body gets washed and prepared for the earth, or have at least read or heard of caring for the gone? The bodies rot under the white paint and hope they are doing it for some good reason. Unless they are buried under glass, well, then they are waiting for some curious hand to open them up and let them crumble into a black whisp, as though they had never been there at all.

THE ARROW AND THE TURTLE

DAVE GREGORY

The arrow I aimed at the sky had a silver metal tip, white shaft and red feathers on the end. "That's called fletching," my dad explained. He'd lived in the Sheffield Orphanage as a kid and never owned a bow and arrow but learned archery from his friend, Mickey McNevin. Using mud, they painted a target on a tree in McNevin's backyard. It was too easy, so they tried shooting into a gap – no wider than a finger – in a stone wall only inches taller than they were. When my dad finally got one through, it raced across the neighbor's garden, pierced a ripe tomato and embedded in the left knee of seventy-year-old Gerald Butters, who was pruning the hedge. Tomato pulp made the wound look worse. Although true, my father's defense – that he wasn't aiming at anything – didn't absolve him. Mr. Butters limped for the rest of his life.

My dad told me this story after buying me a bow and arrow set in 1950. I was twelve. He made me promise to only aim at solid, non-living targets. So, I went with Monty Donlevy and painted a mud circle on an old barn outside town. We were bored after two days.

Alone in my backyard, I tried shooting the arrow straight up. I wanted to send it so high it disappeared.

With each pull, I watched the arrow shrink to a tiny black dot but it always stopped climbing, tilted and came down so fast I rushed under the back stairs for safety.

Holding the bow steadier, pulling harder, I finally did it. I shot the arrow twice as high as the Clarence Street Bridge. Maybe three times. That little black dot just shrank until it vanished into a cloudy sky. I stood in the open, watching, waiting for it to land but it never came back. Fifteen minutes later, when my dad called me for dinner, I was still waiting.

After supper, I looked round the block, sure I'd find the arrow somewhere – but didn't. I pretended it was still travelling, headed for the stars.

⠿

The turtle arrived in 1947. Big as an upside-down cereal bowl, the shell was dark green, yellow streaks decorated its body, and the underside had a snazzy red and black pattern. I found the turtle crawling beneath some shrubs and instantly felt protective. I fed it lettuce, dug a pond so it could swim and named him Clarence, after the bridge. Every other day, I used a hose to refill the pond. Clarence must have been happy because he stayed until fall.

Don't know where he went for the winter but I was thrilled, next spring, when he returned. I never doubted it was the same turtle. He crawled under the fence and shuffled toward me, fast as his little legs could carry him. He stood still while I ducked into the house but restarted once I came out with lettuce.

Around that time, the French people moved in upstairs. We rented the ground floor of that big old house but theirs was a separate unit, accessed by a flight of wooden stairs out back. I never thought much of the family: a mum, dad and two rough-looking boys. It was impossible to understand their accent. Both kids were old enough to shave but didn't and wore a dark smudge above their lips. They had a dog I really liked, who followed me around whenever they let him out unleashed – which happened a lot. Dandy was his name.

They painted the outside stairs and railing yellow – bright as a school bus. It looked ridiculous. Must've got it cheap. They emptied three paint buckets and left them stacked at the end of the driveway. One contained a few wet drops, so I used my finger and painted my initials on the turtle's shell, just above his tail, so I'd always know it was Clarence.

The French people were all "Tabarnak" and "Sacrament" when they realized the paint on the turtle matched their stairs.

When he came back the third year, I spotted my initials but it wasn't Clarence: it was Clarice – she laid eggs beside the pond that spring. Dogs, cats, raccoons, even foxes scavenged for food at night, so I gathered the eggs, thinking they were safer on my screened front porch. I put them in a bucket with sand and placed an old desk lamp above it for warmth. They never hatched. I should have left them alone but thought I was doing the right thing.

Clarice forgave me and returned for a fourth straight year, my initials still bright as the French people's stairs. That was one week before I got the bow and arrow.

▓▓▓

The night I shot the arrow straight up and lost it in the clouds, I remember seeing Clarice munching away near the pond. In the morning, I went round the block and searched everyone's backyard. Three arrows came with the set but I was down to the last one, so I had to find it – Monty accidentally shot the other two onto the roof of that old barn. After an hour, I came home and noticed something different about our lawn. A large, reddish-grey piece of granite always sat by the fence but now it was closer to the house, near the French people's blue Pontiac, which they parked on the grass and seldom moved.

When I got close, I saw Clarice's tiny green and yellow tail sticking out and part of my painted initials. I thought maybe she moved the rock, trying to dig under it, but doubted she was strong enough. Then realization set in. I cringed. My stomach heaved. My knees went weak. Rolling the boulder away, I was horrified to discover she'd been crushed. Poor thing. I'd let her down. Again.

It was sickening. The front half of her dark green shell was shattered. Her insides were a tangled mess of slimy red, green and black organs, connected by beige stringy bits. The ground was wet with blood. I could see Clarice's flattened front legs but her head must've been tucked under a shard of broken shell.

The rock weighed forty pounds or more but I heaved it back where it belonged, then kicked it in rage. I couldn't imagine summer without Clarice, we'd been friends so long. Using a shovel, I moved her to the pond, lowered her in and solemnly heaped soil over her remains. Displaced water soaked the lawn.

I'd no idea why anyone would kill a defenseless turtle but that night the French guy from upstairs – the dad – knocked on our front door. Unshaven, he had a lit, hand-rolled cigarette in the corner of his mouth. There was more "Câlice" and "Baptême." He also said his eldest son's name, pronouncing it like a curse, "Sebastian." The only other word I understood was "merde," which he shouted often.

Everything made sense when I saw my wooden arrow in one hand and white long johns in the other. Rarely a day went by when the French people didn't have underwear on the clothesline. He raised the long johns and poked a finger through a small hole in the crotch. Next he pushed the arrow through. It fit perfectly.

After he left, my mom went to her sewing machine and repaired the long johns in no time. "Since you put the hole in them, you'd better take them to Sebastian and apologize," she said.

Fists clenched, my face hot with anger, I told my parents Sebastian killed Clarice. They wondered how I could be so sure but he was heartless enough, forever aiming his slingshot at wild animals and roaming cats, plus he mumbled "soupe de tortue" each time he came home and found me out back with Clarice. A friend at school confirmed it meant "turtle soup." I spat when he said it.

"Sebastian smashed her with a rock – to get even for the arrow in his long johns. He left her in pieces. The ground's still wet with her blood."

My mother shook her head. My dad said, "Then you brought this on yourself. You killed her eggs last year, now your foolishness killed her. Shooting at the neighbor's clothes – what were you thinking?"

"That's not what happened. It was an accident."

He wasn't listening. "You've got two minutes. Thank your mother for repairing the long johns, then get upstairs and apologize to Sebastian."

My mother handed me the underwear but I had no intention of saying sorry to Clarice's murderer. Outside, I went straight to that big rock, draped the long johns over top, then struggled to lift it. With both hands, I carried the heavy granite in front of me, afraid of dropping it on my toes. In darkness, I waddled to the yellow stairs and climbed one at a time, stopping twice to rest while balancing the stone on the rail. Near the top, I sat and caught my breath, still hungry for revenge. The stars were out. My hands were gritty. A breeze cooled the sweat on my upper lip.

When I reached the landing, I struggled to raise the rock shoulder high. My center of gravity changed and I feared falling backward down the stairs but kept lifting until I had the stone above my head.

Staring at the frosted window in the upper panel of the French family's door, I imagined the satisfaction of seeing it shatter. I pictured the look on Sebastian's face when he saw Clarice's murder weapon on his kitchen floor, with broken glass raining around it.

Then I heard a sound beyond the door. A small animal noise. It was their dog, Dandy. From inside, he heard me on the stairs and came to investigate. Dandy didn't bark. He sniffed, then whimpered an eager little whine, like he was excited I'd come.

One dark corner of my twelve-year-old brain might've thought killing Dandy, with the same rock that killed Clarice, was justifiable but I could never hurt that dog. "Get outta the way, Dandy," I whispered and waited for him to move, while the rock grew heavier.

The dog lingered. I heard him panting.

"Dandy, get away from the door. Go on."

Even if I could throw the rock far enough to clear Dandy's head, there'd still be falling glass. It was too risky. I set the stone on the landing and folded the long johns neatly on top: a white flag of surrender. Through the door, I whispered goodbye to Dandy and retreated. He yelped while I crossed the backyard to kneel under the shrubs, in the wet grass near Clarice's grave.

When the upstairs door opened, Dandy and Sebastian came out and stood in the slash of light. Yellow paint and white underwear glowed at their feet. Dandy sniffed the rock then raised his head to look for me. Sebastian whispered, "Tabarnak," then took Dandy and the long johns inside.

A minute later, Sebastian returned wearing boots. Older and stronger than me, he carried the rock with little effort and dropped it where he first found it.

"Mange la merde," he said. He had no idea I was there but the words were meant for me. *Eat shit.* Probably his favorite meal, besides turtle soup.

BICYCLE THEFT IN THE NEIGHBORHOOD

SARAH CARLETON

The kids who are elastic as bouncing balls
roll with the punches, land and jump back higher,
eyes clear, undaunted by the fall.

The ones who swallow worry suddenly tire,
tummies knotted. They don't know how
to roll with the punches, land and jump back higher,

but croak polite goodbyes, then crack the door and out
they slip, without their bikes, to walk on home.
Tummies knotted, they don't know how

to ignore the bitter dread, so claim it as their own.
But let's talk about the kids who won't let go
or slip—without their bikes—to walk on home.

They sharpen swords, perfect their judo
kicks and plan the fight alone.
Let's talk about these kids who won't let go,

who kiss your cheek so fierce it hurts the bone,
ignoring elastic friends and bouncing balls.
They feel so soft they harden and wheel forth only
with wary eyes and armor dented by the fall.

THE ARCHAEOLOGISTS

JAKE BRANIGAN

My father often referred to Lexi and Emilia as my "girl-cousins," cementing in my mind from an early age that they were different. I was weeks shy of thirteen that summer, and Lexi and Emilia, at sixteen and seventeen respectively, were like foreign creatures of great experience. Whereas my girl-cousins occasionally stumbled into the type of trouble that activated the gears of the family-reunion gossip mill, I was a young saint in training. They got piercings you couldn't pay a jewelry store clerk to administer, while I wasn't allowed in the mall unchaperoned. My mother had left, but their father was dead. Most significantly, they were girls.

It was early July at First Landing State Park in Virginia Beach, and the three of us were squeezed together in the teen's cabin waiting out a storm. I observed them from my usual spot—a silent corner of the far couch, still only half the distance you could flick a stink bug. Lexi kicked up her stubby leg, smeared an oak leaf off her shoe onto a fireplace brick, and shook rain from her hair. In dereliction of her babysitting duties, she had just returned from supplying the neighboring cabin with Chutes and Ladders and a deck of playing cards. Emilia sat cross-legged at the particle board dining table reading a magazine and digging with splayed fingers through a bowl of trail mix. "Next year," Lexi said, one last drag of her sole against the bricks, "they're gonna make you go out to Friday-night dinner. You'll be a *grownup*."

Emilia leaned over the trail mix for closer inspection and extracted one small almond. "No way I'm coming next year."

"Like mom would leave you home." A few years back the three of them had fled for Denver, becoming the first of us to cross the Virginia state line and mean it.

"Won't be her choice anymore," Emilia said, an irritated squint as she flipped a page, misplacing her blame upon some celebrity victim of a *Seventeen* photo shoot.

"Be sure to tip me off before you tell her that." Lexi reached across Emilia to grab their shared iPod, inserted one earbud, and began clicking through the library. Standing beside the table—though there was an empty seat across from her sister—Lexi was as tall as Emilia was sitting down, and Emilia was no giant.

Joining them simply did not strike me as a possibility, though there was nothing stopping me besides an extra-large salad bowl turned upside-down in the center of the floor. Lexi had trapped a spider underneath it just an hour earlier.

They flurried through a dozen cryptic conversations in as many minutes. I missed the subject of what would become their most significant conspiracy while in awe of a half-pint liquor bottle Lexi produced from under her knee-length t-shirt. Baggy clothes were integral to hiding contraband, and their mother—my Aunt Beth—would be missing an important ingredient to this year's Rum Chiller Popsicles. Emilia slid an empty coffee mug forward, and Lexi poured. Ostensibly, I'd been invited to bunk in the teen's cabin because I was the sole member of my age group, stranded between the little kids and my older girl-cousins. In retrospect, Aunt Beth just didn't trust her daughters.

I remained captivated by this criminal activity until Emilia's passive-aggressive throat clearing snapped me out of it. "That's dumb." She took an easy sip of the liquor. "Just because we buried it doesn't mean it's supposed to *stay* there."

Lexi reached into her collar and came out with a crisp pack of cigarettes. She lit one, dragged on it, then blew smoke over Emilia's head. "Do you even remember what's inside?"

"Some of it. Some of the things."

With a snap of her thumb, a premature sprinkle of ash fell onto a paper plate, then Lexi turned her head in what seemed like slow motion and locked onto me. I scanned the room for another object of attention. She faced Emilia again and shook her head. "You won't be able to handle it."

"Handle what? It's just some shit in a box."

Lexi's tone shifted into one that suggested she was, in fact, the big sister: "Then why, exactly, should we go?"

The chair creaked as Emilia pulled an ankle in tighter. She looked down at the overturned salad bowl. The spider imprisoned there was a real monster, so big you could see its individual hairs. Maybe, like me, she was hoping it hadn't escaped. "I've been bored all week and we have nothing better to do."

"Right. Then we'll have to steal Mom's car."

Emilia winced. "*Borrow*. For a little longer than we let on, maybe. You're dramatic."

Lexi ignored this accusation the way a cow ignores a fly crawling across its eyeball. With her cigarette-free hand, she scooped some trail mix, funneled it into her mouth, and chewed. "Benny's coming." She looked at me for the second time that day. "Right?"

I straightened my posture, realized it gave away my eagerness, then slouched again. "Totally."

"Holy shit," said Emilia. "It talks."

"He'll add some validity." Lexi stepped toward me, only to toe-tap the bowl. Despite the patter of rain I heard something scurry underneath. I hoped I did. Otherwise it was under my chair waiting for me. "We'll tell our mom it's your idea."

I nodded. "Cool." Then a moment later, "What idea?"

The weather cleared by late morning, and my twenty or so relatives—aunts, uncles, cousins, and second-cousins of some confusing removal, whose names even then I sometimes failed to summon—congregated at the end of the lane. Uncle Paul threw a tarp into the bed of his old F-150 and let the hose run. He sprayed his chubby five-year-old son, Leon, and with Leon's hair wet you could see the jagged scars running along his skull like an airplane view of a river basin, the result of Paul's now deceased Labrador not appreciating the addition of baby Leon to the family. Paisley, who was at least a year too old to be bare from the waist up, got the hose too, and I looked away as she rubbed water up and down her chest and over her nipples. Uncle Timmy stood alone between the truck and the picnic table, arms crossed, either lost in thought or safeguarding to prevent any of this joy from leaking toward his own two sons, who sat mute at the picnic table, well aware that fun was rarely permitted. Aunt Martha talked loudly with Aunt Mickey, who was either too kind or not cunning enough to avoid being cornered by Martha, something my father was masterful at. I'd never in my life laid eyes on Aunt Martha's ex-husband, Tim—not to be confused with no-fun Uncle Timmy—but he seemed like a perfectly normal person as he chatted with hose-wielding Paul and tossed handfuls of water at the little ones. This pleasant image was inconsistent with the fact that within the last few days I'd seen almost every adult pull a counterpart aside and whisper, "Did you hear Tim is going to stop by? No, *Martha's* Tim." The revelation drew wide-eyed silence, except in the case of Cousin Dan, the most alcoholic of the bunch. He laughed.

Numerous other family members sat at the picnic tables and traded plastic tubs of deli section side dishes. I passed them and entered my father's cabin where I knew I'd find him. Alone.

He was peering out the back window and into the woods, two fingers cracking the blinds like a nosey neighbor. "Close the door soft," he said without turning around. His cabin was identical to mine, but it felt barren, like I'd stepped not into a rented living space but rather into a cage that housed my father, like the wiry domiciles of his Cockatoo and African Grey Parrot back home, or that of the hamster he'd bought me without asking, which quickly became obese because I was entertained by the way it chewed. But those cages at least had colorful ropes and tubes. My father didn't have much other than his fingers in the blinds.

"There's a tree swallow walking along the banister. Great colors. Looks like he's wearing one of those dark blue blazers." My father, on the other hand, was wearing one of his work t-shirts for some reason. I'd asked him once when I was little if him being a plumber meant I had to be one, too. He'd said, "No. I do this because it's the most money anyone will ever let me make for this family."

"There she goes." He released the blinds and turned around.

"Emilia is going to drive me to get a hermit crab," I said.

"They're not much for pets."

"Want one anyway." I didn't.

"You asking for money?"

I felt my back pocket instinctively. "I have ten bucks." My wallet held nothing but a ten-dollar bill and a scrap torn from a birthday card my mother had sent me six months prior. A phone number where I could reach her. I'd called only once. A man picked up.

"Okay. Get a big one." He eased onto the couch, cracked open a spy novel, but refrained from looking down at it. "How's the kid's cabin?"

"The teen's cabin."

"You're a teen?"

"About."

He nodded. "Fine. Teen's cabin. Girl-cousins playing nice?"

I returned the nod. I was included now, on this mission at least.

"Be sure to thank your Uncle Morrey for footing the bill." The *your* he inserted before mentioning a family member was a way of separating himself from my mother's side. "Don't be too long."

I turned, intending to leave, but escaping my father's cage felt oddly cruel, despite us being like different species in the same terrarium, forced to cross one another's path on occasion but otherwise happy to be nestled in separate corners. My about-face continued into a three-sixty, and he cocked an eyebrow at this odd dance move. "Everyone's eating lunch out there," I said.

He unfolded a dog ear within the book. "Hear 'em. I ate." This put an end to the longest conversation I'd had with my father since getting to the beach.

Outside, Leon was dunking his trail-blazed head into a few inches of water. Paisley hugged herself, not to cover her nakedness but because the brisk, post-rain afternoon had her shivering. The hose lay dead by the truck's back wheels. Ex-husband Tim sat alone on the bumper staring into the trees while the rest of them got at the potato salad. I went to ask Paisley if she needed help down when Aunt Beth appeared at my side like a skilled illusionist.

"Lexi says you want to see the ships in Norfolk."

This was not part of the cover story. "No," I said. Her chin tilted upward. "I mean, yes, but I want to get a hermit crab. Then see the ships."

She studied me for one uncomfortable second, then quick-stepped back toward her cabin where Lexi waited by the minivan. Aunt Beth removed a set of keys from Lexi's hand and shook her head theatrically. I approached when it was all clear, Emilia on my tail. "Who blew it?" Emilia said.

Reaching into her shirt, Lexi almost removed her pack of cigarettes, but remembered where she was and poked it back down. "It's still on. Minor change in schedule."

Ten minutes before nine that night, I was at the table playing a one-man game of Scrabble when Emilia's phone buzzed. She flipped it open, read a text, pulled out her earbuds and clunked down the heavy iPod onto the corner of the board, shifting my tiles. "Let's go."

Outside, I crawled into the back of the van, and Lexi kept the engine silent as she cruised us out of the park, then roared it when we hit Shore Drive.

※

I was an introvert back then, but my silence was also strategic. If I didn't bother my girl-cousins, I'd be allowed to remain in their presence. To risk annoying them was to risk excommunication, so my silence continued, but because of this I was in the dark as far as specifics. I had, however, eavesdropped and inferred my way toward understanding the basic plan—we were driving to the northern edge of Virginia to excavate a time capsule from their childhood back yard. After ten minutes of internal deliberation, and during a momentary lull in Emilia's diatribe against her mother, I broke my code and spoke up from the quiet shadows of the back seat: "Do we have something to dig with?"

They were startled, having probably forgotten I was there, but their surprise transformed into nervous laughter. "Good call, Benny," Emilia said. She waved a finger back at me, as if throwing salt over her shoulder. "That's why we carry you around."

We were locked inside a gift shop called The Undertow for all of five minutes before Emilia's flirtation with the taller of the two European employees transitioned from practical to sincere. They'd been closing up shop when our headlights crept up their shins. Emilia hopped from the van with an exaggerated bounce in her step, and the tall one spied the pop and wave of her frilly miniskirt and since then hadn't let her further away than the length of one sleeveless arm. She pulled at locks of her hair and laughed at his stilted, near-proficient English, whereas I think Lexi was only chatting up the shorter one—propped on his elbows in a suave lean over the counter—in an attempt to get the beach shovel for free.

The first thing I'd noticed inside the store was the stack of clear lunchbox-sized cages, inside each an inch of sand, a useless miniature beach umbrella, and a hermit crab. I tapped on a few but the crabs were sluggish, so I went searching for the toy section and found it against the opposite wall, past the three-for-fifteen tank tops, the shot glasses, and the painted knick-knacks all emblazoned with *Virginia Beach* either in a blocky font or a twirling script. The least expensive shovel wouldn't withstand the digging of real earth, but I found one that didn't bend much against my knee. When I returned to the front of the store, Emilia was asking her emaciated, moderately tanned Euro-friend if there were beaches where he was from. I thought he answered, "Snow,"—as in, that's all that exists in his homeland—but he'd actually said, "No...that is why we are here. For beaches and for American girls." He grinned like the antagonist in a Hanna Barbera cartoon, like he wanted to eat her, but Emilia seemed okay with it.

Still multiple years away from any sex life of my own, but plenty old enough to understand the tone of this conversation, I was overcome with the desire to knee him in the balls, saving Emilia from something I understand now she had the right to want. This was not the first daydream in which I prevented some terrible fate from befalling my cousins. Where I was strong.

Emilia's friend excused himself and went behind the counter, where the two employees whispered unnecessarily in a foreign language, then the shorter one made a grand announcement in an accent even more difficult to understand despite the brevity of his message: "We have weed."

Behind the store, sandwiched between the building and a chain link fence, Emilia took longer drags from the joint than the guys did. This was my first marijuana siting, but in a confusing way the aroma was redolent, as if I'd smelled it long ago, maybe in my dreams. "Can the little man?" Emilia's friend asked her, but I demurred. Lexi didn't partake, but she sucked down one cigarette and immediately lit another. The shorter guy slinked away and returned with a flask, and Lexi, the only remaining sober person with a driver's license, took a slug from it and I thought maybe now we're in trouble.

Emilia's friend sat down on the stoop, and my cousins stood directly over him. He looked skyward into their faces. "You two will come to a party...tonight to our party," he said, then corrected, "little man, also."

The short one was leaning against the building, and when Lexi ashed her cigarette some of it alighted on his bare toes. "And who, might I ask, will be at this party?"

"Roommates," the short guy said, swigging again, his eyelids heavy, like maybe they'd been at this before we'd arrived. He handed me the flask and I passed it to Lexi.

"Any girls?" she asked.

"Yes. Of course," the stoop-sitter said. "Two of you." He pointed at my cousins one after the other, the same eat-you smile on his face.

"*No* of course two of us," Lexi said. "We've got some shit to dig up."

He worked to interpret this strange American idiom, failed to do so, and instead placed his hand on Emilia's calf. "Just you then, why not?"

A scenario flashed through my mind: Emilia agreeing, promising it would only take an hour, a battle brewing between my cousins, a stalemate, and Emilia finally dragging us to some strange den because Lexi would never let her go alone. My pulse quickened. But none of this played out. Emilia stepped around him, reached for the door. "Next time, boys."

"Wait," he said, and he reached up and pinched her skirt, held it as she took a step, laying bare an inch of cream-colored skin south of her tan line. I had no awareness of my own movement until I heard the crack of the shovel's head against his wrist. He gasped. I'd swatted him good. The short one laughed nervously and got cursed for it. The taller one rose and, terrified, I only meant to hold out the shovel defensively, but it connected, a stiff shot somewhere just below the belt. He grumbled in his language, leapt up, slapped the shovel from my hand, then gave me a light push on the shoulder the way an annoyed older brother might. Lexi hip-checked me aside, swung overhand, and stamped his chest with the cherry of her cigarette.

Recoiling, he swiped at the fresh hole in his shirt like it was a hornet, a flourish of gravely, uninterpretable language off his tongue.

"Touch him again," Lexi dared, her cigarette pointed like a dagger. Off to the side, the short one stuck his hands up like this was a dark-alley mugging. Lexi reached back and pulled me forward, nearly tossed me back into the shop as Emilia, with cloudy-eyed laughter, held open the door. "Crazy bitch," was the only English to be heard as it shut behind us.

I snagged a replacement shovel while Emilia jogged to the front with the mirth of an escaped infant and clicked open the lock. When

I pulled the solitary ten dollar bill from my wallet, the scrap from my mother's birthday card fluttered to the floor and Lexi picked it up. "You little pimp," she said, inspecting the phone number. I snatched it from her as the back door chunked closed, then dropped the ten onto the entrance mat. The stack of hermit crabs called to me for a moment, but they were never the point. "Come on, killer," Lexi said, and I followed her out, where in the few seconds between the cigarette stabbing and our escape the sky had unleashed a torrent of rain.

▓▓▓

A bottle inside me had broken, and I was pouring everywhere. I told jokes. We sang songs. When they asked if I was a lady's man I captivated them with a dramatic retelling of the only breasts I'd ever touched—after a science lesson on reproduction my metal-mouthed desk partner had convinced me to meet her beside the Coke machine where I experienced the small lumps underneath her sweatshirt and said nothing but thank you afterward. We yammered like this for three hours, except during a monsoon that hit near Occoquan, at which time Lexi demanded silence, craned her neck to focus through the windshield she was fogging worse with nervous tobacco smoke, less escaping out the cracked window than there was rain coming in. Before I knew it, we were parked up the street from their old house, the downpour again so heavy we couldn't leave the van, or maybe we didn't want to.

They had reclined their seats all the way back, and I was sprawled along the bench behind them. We ranked the family members from most to least annoying, arguing over only a few, and during a rare pause Lexi took a swig from the flask she'd apparently stolen. The rain sounded like one massive thing beating against the car. Lexi said, "You think your mom's dead in a ditch somewhere, Benny?"

"Jesus," Emilia whined.

But I knew the phrase, and why she used it. It was a cliché thrown around at last year's reunion—*she could be dead in a ditch for all we know*—adults incorrectly assuming that kids can't hear anything once they've turned the corner. And though I had a basic understanding of

107

addiction at the time, I was sure she wasn't dead, and I told them so. She'd been alive six months before, at least, when she'd sent me the birthday card, but I didn't mention that.

Perhaps Lexi misinterpreted that her question had hurt me. "If it makes you feel better, our dad's definitely dead in a ditch."

"Jee-sus!" Emilia squealed again.

"What? I'm not wrong. Think about it."

The rain kept on. Eventually I fell asleep, slept straight through, and woke to a silent break of day, save the melody of Emilia's cell phone. "We just borrowed the car ten minutes ago, Mom. Breakfast. Then the beach. Relax. Back in a while."

▓▓▓

In the back yard there was only six feet of level ground before a dimpled hill rose as high as the house's roof, but the trees and brush atop it gave us cover. The earth was rain-softened, but Emilia still snapped off the shovel's head within the first few tries. A triangle of sharp plastic remained below the handle, so we were left with a trowel—something we would have been better off shopping for to begin with. I helped grind away at the perimeter of each hole with a stick until Emilia gave up and started a new one a few inches over.

"Probably more to your left," Lexi said. She was facing away from us, sitting out in the open, her butt certainly wet. She looked back and pointed. "The middle of the fort would've been about here." She stared again at the house like it wasn't there at all. Like there was nothing but open field for miles.

"You two had a fort?"

"Out of branches and twigs," Emilia said, stabbing the dirt.

"Our carpet was flattened cardboard covered in three layers of duct tape." Lexi's voice floated off. "Could've just found some real carpet."

"How fucking deep could I have buried something as an eight-year—" Emilia gasped. Instantly thrilled. She poked hurriedly then excavated by hand. The box wasn't much bigger than a cell phone by today's standards. She wiped away smudges of dirt to reveal the white face of Hello Kitty. "I was sad about using this box. It was my

108

favorite." She shook it. Tink, tink, tink went the world's smallest padlock. "Shit," she said.

Lexi, who had appeared beside us, took over. At arm's length she pushed with one hand and pulled at the padlock with the other thumb and pointer, like an attempt at shooting an impossible arrow. With a grunt of effort, the lock's metal curve sliced through the thin, worn tin of the latch and the box shot from her grasp and spilled its contents along the ground.

On her knees, Emilia frantically reached for all of the objects at once, but her indecisive palms only hovered over them, like a voodoo priestess reading the bones, until she carefully picked up and unfolded a two-dollar bill. Sections of it were stained, others perfect. I handed her a mini-troll doll, the bottom carved out to fit over a pencil eraser. She put down the bill and carefully unmated its pink hair. "Hey soldier," Lexi said, reaching down to collect the green army man. She touched her fingertip to its flimsy, curved rifle. All that remained on the ground was a bundle of half-sized colored pencils secured by a thick rubber band. Emilia contemplated them, then right-sided the box and with extreme care removed a folded piece of off-white sketch paper that had been stuck at the bottom. She unfurled it like a map. Much of the drawing was mildewed and washed away, yet the paper was dry, brittle-looking. Emilia only inspected it a moment before folding it again.

I asked to see it. It was significantly damaged, but I could make out an artistically coherent background of grass, sky, and portions of a house. Also, an arm extending out from a dress, fingers open and waiting. The paper was rippled with water damage, but less fragile than I'd thought.

"What?" Lexi spat, startling me. Staring down at Emilia, who was now sullen, Lexi slapped her hands aggressively against her thighs. "What did you think you'd find? A magic cure in a dumb fucking box?" Her anger was instantaneous, sharp, and genuine, but I remember noticing even in that unsure moment that it felt distinctly rehearsed. She'd known all along that this was what she'd end up saying.

Emilia was not crying. Not even a mist in her eyes. But the sight of tears would have been a relief. Downcast stare. Wilting expression. Her face alone carried a sorrow that boiled my gut.

"No way, bitch. Not right now," Lexi said, grabbing Emilia's arm. "We're out of here, then." They were down the hill before I could finish stuffing into my pockets everything they'd left behind.

Dead silence, the first few minutes in the van. "Should I turn here?" Lexi said, her eyes off the road and on Emilia, her tone anything but softened. "At the light?" Emilia ignored her. "Why not," Lexi said. A car horn blared as she merged late into the turn lane. Silence again for a while. Behind them, my knees tucked to my chest, I tried to make myself feel like I wasn't there. Then, "What about up here? Huh?" She took the turn wide and fast. "Here we go. This is what you were afraid to ask for."

We drove into the cemetery via some street other than the main entrance, because I was unaware initially that is was a cemetery at all. Just a maze of thin, curving paths, and in the middle of one curve no more significant than the others we'd navigated, Lexi pulled up into the grass and yanked the keys from the ignition, extinguishing the vibrations in my seat and leaving only an unwelcome stillness. She got out. Emilia remained, sitting like a girl in church: stiff, chin raised indignantly, but unconcerned. No visible remnant of her sorrow from just twenty minutes before. I watched her until, for no discernable reason other than the fact that fifteen seconds had passed, she popped her door.

Lexi, her rigid arms swinging, marched half a dozen paces in front of Emilia, with me a few yards back at the tail. She seemed to get shorter as the earth sloped to reveal a litter of gravestones beyond. This was another moment where I chose not to question, nor speak at all. My mindset, even if I wasn't mature enough at that age to define it, was that people would narrate for me if they were inclined to. Otherwise, if it mattered that I know, I'd learn what was happening eventually without bothering anyone. But more importantly, in this instance I had to play it cool, because I felt I was being included in something meaningful. Perhaps for the first time.

Ahead of us, Lexi slowed. Then she stopped, as if her feet had reached a precipice, or she'd encountered an invisible wall. A weak sound, impossible to interpret at first, came from her throat. Then she bent fully at the waist, and with her elbows driven into her thighs and her hands masking her face, she sobbed. A few with breath, then a rolling and uncontrolled wave.

I was stunned. Emilia was not. With a firm grip on Lexi's shoulder, Emilia unbent her sister, hooked an arm around her and sent their now combined bodies moving forward. Lexi continued to wail, and though she was somewhat guided, she proceeded on her own power. I stuffed my hands in my pockets and followed at a respectable distance, considered stopping and facing the opposite direction until I was eventually collected again, but just then Emilia's free arm rotated backward and her fingers wiggled for me. I grasped her hand and she glued mine hard against her hip.

Emilia pulled us along, somehow both forceful and incredibly tender. Lexi sobbed, but she didn't balk. Her legs carried her toward something that she almost couldn't handle, but her choice was to keep moving. A few years after this I would start to make more friends. I'd get involved in sports and by the end of high school you could argue I was popular. I drank beer with my boys on the weekend. We'd lean on our lockers but straighten up when hot girls walked by in pairs. Once, at three in the morning, we stopped the car in the center lane of the Fairfax County Parkway and jumped out for a push-up contest cut short by a barreling grocery truck, and sometimes we'd punch each other in the shoulder as hard as we could and not one of us ever flinched, and often within these moments, as I was blinded by a grocery truck's headlights or just before a fist smashed into the tender flesh of my upper arm, I would remember the cemetery and how Emilia and Lexi putting one foot forward and then the next was the truest feat of strength I ever witnessed in my life.

I had no memory of my late uncle, but when we reached the headstone his first name felt warmly familiar. Cade. The letters were carved out in rough contrast to the polished maroon of the stone's surface. We looked down at it, still a three-person chain. Lexi's cheeks were high on her face, eyes squinted, but tears held at bay. She'd been five when he died from a rare blood disease.

Our circuit broke as Emilia knelt to feel the ridge of a letter, or to remove a sticky shard of grass. Remembering the contents of my pockets, I raised the folded parchment and the colored pencils, shook them to imply, *you know what I mean?* Emilia dragged the tilted lead lightly across the paper, opposite side of the drawing, capturing her father's first and last initials like ghosts slowly revealing themselves to the haunted. She showed it to Lexi, who eventually folded it and tucked it inside her shirt next to her cigarettes, near where her heart was beating.

▓▓▓

Back in Virginia Beach there were no drops falling but the air was so thick with mist that Lexi had the wipers going in a slow, mesmerizing trade off. We tunneled through to their mom's cabin, and the dream I'd been living in those last fifteen hours dispersed into the mist as the van tilted off the road and the keys released with a scrape and a click.

"You better run for it, Benny," Lexi said. "She's gonna be mad."

"Flee, Benny. Flee," said Emilia.

The creak-and-slap of the screen door was impossible to miss, as was the threat yelled from the porch. My cousins looked at one another before exiting the van in perfect synchronicity, and the slam of the car doors toppled the green army man that had ridden home on the dash. I climbed into the cockpit and righted him. Emilia had forgotten her cell phone.

I rehearsed silently for a minute. No need to remove my wallet. I'd memorized the number, along with most of my mother's handwritten message. To fool my father, she'd disguised the birthday card as having been sent by one of her sisters, and she requested I dispose of it. Initially, I'd wondered why she was scared of him, but I grew to understand that she believed her leaving, her giving in to addiction, was a weakness. You can fear your husband, and you can fear your family, but there's safety in your child not knowing how to do

112

anything but love.

It went to voicemail, which had been my hope. "Mom, I used to ask Dad when you were coming back, and he said he didn't know, but I could tell he wished you would. I'm sorry I never called before. You probably don't want to come home. But if you do, and you think you can't, you can." I snapped the phone shut and left it on the seat for Emilia to find.

Around the corner, I could hear the commotion from inside Aunt Martha's cabin, where we ate lunch when the weather was bad. Martha's ex-husband, Tim, sat in a rocking chair alone on the porch. Forced out or by choice? I wondered. He waved. "Hi, Benny."

"Hi, Tim."

"Head's up, your old man is peeved."

I thanked him, waved as I passed, and thought it better to grab a shower before encountering my father, but I didn't get the chance. As I stepped foot in the teen's cabin, he stood up from the table and met me dead center of the room.

"Better have an award-winning excuse."

"They needed me. I wanted to be there to protect them." It was a cheap play, because I knew it would work on him. He kept his stance rigid, but a few key muscles in his face relaxed. I took advantage and went on the offensive. "Why aren't you over at the lunch cabin?"

"I'm busy waiting here goddamn worried that you're—"

"Yeah, but you could have waited over *there*. Where everybody else is."

He thrust his chin out while he calculated. Was I being defiant? Should he push back or give way? "When you get a little older I'll explain some things."

One adventure with my cousins wasn't enough to change the fact that I was a quiet kid. I wasn't yet able to look him in the eye and say I know that mental health disorders and drug addiction cause stress on everyone involved. That you thought you knew what was best to help mom and other people in these other cabins thought different. You were wrong, but you still drive me down to Virginia Beach every year and lock yourself away in a cage to provide me an opportunity to

113

be part of this family.

Instead I said, "Did you touch the bowl?" It was at our feet, close enough for either of us to kick. He said no. "Dad, you've got to check out this monster. You're gonna love him." I crouched, looked up at him and smiled. He slid an inch backward as I placed both hands on the dome. Before I lifted it I thought, Don't be dead. Don't just scurry away. Jump four feet in the air. Crawl up one of our legs. Do something we'll remember forever.

THE HOUSES OF GOD

BRANDON NOEL

He should get a ticket for that, my neighbor Clyde rolled back
down from the sidewalk, next to me smoking on the porch.
His complaint? Some car blew right through the 4-way stop sign

at the end of our street, where the United Methodist Church sits,
on the corner. I went to high school with a Methodist girl, who said
they had a special room with just a dirt floor—called it the holy place.

I thought it was weird. Like the largest door you've ever seen or the
sense
of dreadful strangeness when you first realize old people used to be
young.
The annexation of self, the horror cosmic, the deep-fakes effect of
aging,

the uncanny valley of your childhood voice and its tonal changes.

I wondered if it's what made them Methodists, like how I was Pentecostal

and spoke-in-tongues or danced in the aisles. She thought that was weird.

Some bare earthen room inside me—afraid and full of the unspeakable

words in her. They know exactly who I am. The unutterable spirit between.

Clyde pulled out of his driveway. His electric motorized chair strapped

to a dark grey Jeep Cherokee. He and his wife worshiped at a new church-plant

inside the fellowship hall of another church. A nesting-doll of temples. They use

the side entrance, hang banners with their name. I sat outside till noon.

LOCATED NEAR ANOTHER

K. SHAWN EDGAR

Hey, Margery Divine. The Cross Orbweaver spiders have laced our gardens with utilitarian grace. Insects beware. The brown, orange, and black eight-legs of October are rising. And thriving in their dangling diners. We fear not as humans, for the cross spider is a useful sentry. A friend. And as neighbors we create connections like webs, for balance with our surroundings, and a mutable flowing sense of unity. Between the flowering plants and the shade of tall trees, we exist now together.

THE MOST MEMORABLE NEIGHBORS WE HAD IN OUR 20S

CÉLÈSTE FOHL

1. Mr. Upstairs, who played The Mighty Mighty Bosstones at 8:00 in the morning and slept in a hammock. He invited us to climb out his window and drink beers on the roof of our 5-plex. A chemical engineer with a bushy beard and a barrel chest, his routine was to save money for a few months, quit his job, hike the Appalachian Trail or the PCT, come home, get his job back, and repeat the process. He made a stupid amount of money and owned almost nothing. After he moved to DC for a girl, we talked about visiting him and never did.

2. Ms. Across the Hall, who tacked up flags and bandanas in her windows. She began dating our friend Megan's boyfriend roughly three days before he broke up with Megan. After that, his stupid pickup truck with its pink racing stripes and

faded *Tesla > Edison* bumper sticker was always parked out front, and Megan would always ask, "Is he there?" before coming over.

3. Ms. Downstairs, who painted the mural down the street and stuffed her windows with house plants. Often, we heard her fucking her boyfriend loudly and at length. Once, in the middle of it—right in the middle of it—they got into an argument and he stormed out. She put on a record, and he didn't come by for several weeks. We couldn't look her in the eye after that. We'd never witnessed something so private in the life of a near-stranger.

4. Mr. Next Door, who was dying of cancer. Our cat used to walk across the railing between our two balconies and meow at his sliding glass door. He'd let our cat in and feed him, and our cat would play with his cat, who was small and sweet and had lost the tips of her ears to frostbite and was the only other cat ours ever liked.

5. Mr. Back Unit, who spent most days drinking PBR on his stoop. He and his girlfriend, who lived with him at first and then didn't, had an infant daughter with a heart defect. They'd moved to the city to be near the children's hospital. When the baby wasn't doing well, he'd come home late, alone and so drunk he couldn't get his key in the lock. We'd hear him out our open window (no A/C), grumbling and pounding on the door, and one of us would have to go downstairs to let him in. Much later, in our 30s, we saw him, strung out and gray-faced, on the steps of the neighborhood convenience store, United Dairy Farmers. We knew it was him, but he didn't know us.

FOURTH OF JULY

LIZ DEGREGORIO

I wanted to compliment the woman's
dog, who was so calm as fireworks exploded
in our neighborhood.

But just then, I heard her on the phone:
"Four years ago, we were
together. We were
together for the fireworks."

I knew that a stranger's shallow compliment
was not going to fix the woman's
broken heart.

BERMUDA

JUDITH TURNER-YAMAMOTO

The day Emogene met Rosa Lee she heard her before she saw her. Heard the screen door slam, the quick click-slap, click-slap of her mules on the sidewalk. Emogene turned clear around on the porch swing to watch her. Tiny waist and pale shoulders shown off above the full sweep of a pink dress that wrapped around her like fresh spun cotton candy. Hair as red as the new T-Bird convertible parked in her driveway. She minced back and forth, eyes locked on the ground.

"No place within fifty miles of here to go dressed up like that," Emogene's mother had said, sweeping the porch one Friday evening while Emogene watched for Rosa Lee and Larry to leave. But when they came out her mother held her broom still and watched too. Rosa Lee wobbled down the steps in her spike heels. Laughing, she reached for Larry's arm to steady her. Larry opened the car door for Rosa Lee, folded her skirt around her legs.

"Big ideas for little people." Her mother had slapped her broom at a cobweb slung between the corner rafters. Jealous, Emogene remembered thinking. Her mother was just sorry it wasn't her riding off in a fancy car with a good-looking man.

Emogene held the screen door, closing it softly behind her. If her mother heard, she'd call out, spoiling everything. She wanted to come up on her new neighbor slow, the way you would on a squirrel chewing nuts or a bird pecking at grubs.

"You looking for something?" she called out.

"Oh, Lord." Rosa Lee clutched her sequined bodice. "Where'd you pop up from?"

Emogene pointed to her house. "Next door."

Rosa Lee went back to her looking while Emogene studied her. She was shorter than Emogene, but then, since she'd turned twelve and started growing uncontrollably, that was almost anybody female. There was nothing exceptional about any of the features in Rosa Lee's heart-shaped face, not the small nose or the wide blue eyes, or the tiny mole that floated off to the side of her full mouth. But together they made her seem prettier than she was.

"I can't believe I lost that earring," Rosa Lee said. "Larry just gave them to me. That's what I get for wearing them to go nowhere."

Emogene dropped to her knees, squinted into the darkness under the car. "Is it green?"

"That's it!"

Emogene looked at Rosa Lee from under her left arm. All she could see were long toes, the nails even and polished pink. She had read in one of her fashion magazines that long toes made for a beautiful foot and she could see now this was true. "I can't reach. Maybe if I hit it a rock, it'll fly out on the other side of the car."

"No, let me get the broom." Emogene heard the click-slap of Rosa Lee's heels up the walk. She was back as quickly as she'd gone, holding the broom away from her dress. "Here," she said. "Now you watch what you're doing."

Emogene rolled onto her stomach, swept the earring out from

under the car.

Earring cradled in her palm, Rosa Lee started for the house. She was almost to the steps before she stopped, turned to Emogene.

"You like Pepsi-Colas?"

Emogene shrugged, pretending interest in the dirt on her shirt. She looked at her house. Her mother's bedroom blinds were still drawn. She pictured her laying there, a wet washrag across her eyes. She added up the time left before she would sigh, take off the cloth, and drag herself into the kitchen to start supper. "I can only stay a minute." She followed Rosa Lee into the house, stepping over movie magazines, a pair of roller skates, a broken Slinky.

Rosa Lee headed for the bathroom, the Pepsi forgotten. She grabbed a tissue, gently rubbed the earring. "There, that's more like it, as green as a tropical sea."

Emogene had no idea what a tropical sea looked like. She craned her neck to get a better look. The color was somewhere between blue and green, like something floating in mid-air. Nothing at all like the battleship gray of the ocean at Carolina Beach. She sucked in her breath. "Does water really look like that somewhere?"

"In Bermuda it does." Rosa Lee turned to the cluttered table behind the door, rummaging through its contents. Jars of cream and makeup, bottles of nail polish. Baby dress-colored cotton balls--pink, blue, and yellow--spilled out of a glass candy jar. Combs and brushes and curlers with hair of different colors worked deep into the pink foam. "I guess it's all that pink sand," Rosa Lee said.

"Pink sand," Emogene repeated, thrilled by the possibility. She watched Rosa Lee put on the earrings. The color of her eyes shifted, becoming more green than blue. "Your eyes look like the stones."

"That's just why Larry bought them for me. He says he's going to take me to Bermuda someday just to see my eyes against that sea."

The earrings, the makeup, Rosa Lee's dress. Emogene hadn't known such romance existed outside her mind. How could she get invited back? She settled on the sand bucket and plastic boats under the sink.

"You got kids? Maybe you'd like somebody to babysit."

An open red lipstick in her hand, Rosa Lee sized her up. She turned back to the mirror, rubbed her lips together, dabbed the corners of her mouth with her little finger. "I think that just might work out fine. You be here next Friday, three o'clock sharp."

▓▓▓

"How come you're always so bossy when Mama's around?" Seven-year-old Larry Anthony watched Rosa Lee pull out of the driveway.

Emogene sat on the edge of the couch. Toes perched on the lip of the coffee table, she tried out Rosa Lee's new nail polish. "I can't let on I enjoy being here or your mama will stop paying me." She held her baby toe, steadied the brush loaded with polish. "And if I don't get paid, *my* mama won't let me come over." She sat back and admired the shimmery pink, ignoring the steady racket coming from the corner. "Martin Wendall," she said without looking up, "stop beating on that TV or I'll lock you in your room while we play hopscotch and eat ice cream."

"Pull his hair," Larry Anthony said. "That's what Mama does."

Martin Wendall covered his head with his scrawny arms and went right on kicking.

Emogene lunged for him. In one motion he grabbed the box of chalk on the coffee table and leapt past her for his parents' bedroom.

Larry's picture on the nightstand brought her up short. Last night Emogene had seen him through her bedroom window and the tossing leaves of the maple tree that separated the two houses. He had sat slumped on the bed staring at the floor. Rosa Lee stood before him, hands welded to her hips. Then Rosa Lee moved to the kitchen by the sink, holding her head in her hands. Larry came up behind her. Rosa Lee leaned back against him, reached up to touch his face. When the leaves parted again the house was black. Staring into the darkness, her arms wrapped tight around herself, Emogene had tried hard to picture them rumpling the smooth white taffeta bedspread.

Martin Wendall's small fingers reached from his hiding place beneath the bed, tickled her ankle. Emogene dropped down, lifted the spread. "I was only fooling about locking you in," she said. "Let's go outside so we can hear the ice cream man when he comes."

He slid out from under the bed, threw the chalk box at her. But he fell in step beside her, offering his hand to hold. Wild and tame, that was Martin Wendall. Emogene ran her fingers over his head, brushed away dust motes. His hair was dark brown except for a white-blonde streak that shot across his forehead. When Rosa Lee was babying him, she would say a shooting star had grazed his head. Rosa Lee had the white streak, too. Emogene knew from a picture of Rosa Lee taken when she was eighteen, right before Larry Anthony was born.

Emogene found him outside, drawing perfect squares on the walk. Rosa Lee's hands were so full with Martin Wendall, Larry Anthony had taken to raising himself. Martin Wendall ran over to the driveway, picked out a stone to use for the potsy. Larry Anthony took it from him, threw it on the first square.

"When are you going to your granny's?" asked Emogene.

"Soon as Daddy comes to get us." Balanced on one foot, Larry Anthony bent over to pick up the potsy.

"You sure about that?" Rosa Lee hadn't said anything about Larry coming before she got back.

"Everybody knows it's Friday night," he said in that way he had of talking to her as if she was the child. "Besides, Mama said he'd be early."

"But not before she gets back," she said for her own benefit. This wouldn't be the first time the hour Rosa Lee was supposed to stay gone stretched into two. So far Emogene had managed to avoid meeting Larry. Instead, she listened for him each evening while she set the table for dinner. When he reached the place where the sidewalk turned at a right angle and she could no longer pretend he was walking towards her, she pressed her nose deeper into the wire mesh of the porch screen. Her hands smelled of sweat and corroded metal and something more she couldn't name, something that faded away once Larry was inside the house.

Martin Wendall pulled on her arm. "Come on, the ice cream truck's here, you promised." She followed the boys to the truck, too stirred up to order anything for herself.

The boys went back to hopscotch. Their fudgesicles dripped on the sidewalk, blotching the yellow chalk marks. Emogene sat on the porch steps, arms hugging her bony knees.

"Why aren't you playing?" Larry Anthony asked.

"I can't be playing hopscotch with you," she snapped, irritable with him for reminding her she still did. "What would your Daddy think?"

"Maybe he'll play, too." Martin Wendall wiped the last of his ice cream on his shorts.

"Shut up, Martin Wendall." Larry Anthony jumped in his little brother's square, knocking him off balance.

Larry's car made a sharp turn at the corner. The bottom dropped out of Emogene's stomach as sure as if she stood in the car's path.

Martin Wendall ran to the driveway, latching himself on Larry's leg the instant he was out of the car. Larry Anthony kept right on with his hopscotch.

"Well, hello there." Larry took off his sunglasses, revealing the surprise of hooded pale blue eyes beneath dark brows. "You must be Emogene."

"Uh huh." Emogene looked down at her feet and the glimmering reproach of Rosa Lee's polish.

"You boys behave yourselves?"

Martin Wendall nodded, jumping in a circle around Larry. Larry Anthony didn't look up from where he sat, drawing tight little circles and squares on the sidewalk.

"How much do I owe you, sweetheart?"

"Fifty cents," Emogene mumbled, holding out her hand.

Larry put the money in her palm. She raised her eyes to thank him. He grinned and winked at her. She wished for the steps to open and swallow her whole. When nothing happened, she stood up, busied herself with brushing the seat of her shorts.

Larry reached in his T-shirt pocket for his cigarettes. "Fresh out." He crushed the pack, tossed it on the ground. "Let's run on down to the drugstore before your Mama gets home."

Martin Wendall and Larry Anthony raced to the car. Larry Anthony slid in the back seat; Martin Wendall jumped in front behind the wheel.

"You coming?" Larry said to Emogene, pushing his hair back from his face. "Give you a chance to spend that fifty cents."

"Come on, Emogene!" Martin Wendall yelled, lunging through the car window.

Emogene followed Larry to the car, eyes fastened on the dark hair curling at the nape of his neck. The drugstore was only five blocks away. They would beat Rosa Lee home.

"Get in back with your brother, Martin Wendall." Larry walked around the car, opened the passenger door.

Emogene froze. He turned to look at her. "Well, come on."

She felt her face go red, heard the boys giggle. She hurried around the car.

He got behind the wheel, pulled a bottle of beer from under the seat. He pointed at the glove compartment. "Open that, will you?"

He reached across her, his arm brushing her leg. "There's a church key in here somewhere." He rummaged through papers, a careless tangle of sunglasses. A blue pair belonging to Rosa Lee tumbled out. "Wear them if you want," Larry offered.

She slipped them on, the green of the lenses turning things cool.

Larry gave a low whistle. "Cat's eyes." He turned the rearview mirror in her direction. "Have a look."

"That's okay," she said, careful to stay still. The backs of her legs were already stuck to the seat covers. If she moved, he might hear her skin pull away from the plastic.

He flipped the cap off the beer, started the car. She'd never seen anybody drink before. The whole county was dry, the nearest package store in a town ten miles over the county line.

"Let's go get those cigarettes." Larry backed into the street. He propped the bottle between his legs, shifted into first.

Emogene turned to the back seat. "Let's play stoplight." She'd made the game up for the times they rode along with Rosa Lee to the store. "The one with the most lights wins."

"I'm red," Larry Anthony said.

"Green, green!" cried Martin Wendall.

"Fine," Emogene said in her best babysitting voice. "I'll be yellow."

Larry looked over at her. "Then I bet you win." He floored the gas pedal, making a hard-left turn as the light at the intersection turned from yellow to red. The boys collapsed in the corner, shrieking.

Martin Wendall lunged forward, grabbed Larry around the neck. "Green, green!" he squealed in his father's ear.

Sliding toward Larry, Emogene held on to the dash. "Bet you never knew your game could be so much fun," he said, pushing her upright.

"I don't like going fast," she managed to get out.

"Most women don't. Now Rosa Lee, she loves it as much as I do."

"Red, Daddy, do red!" Larry Anthony screamed.

"No, green, Daddy!" Martin Wendall's feet pumped with excitement, jarring the front seat.

They sped on with Emogene counting off the blocks, her bottom lip held tight between her teeth. She relaxed into her seat when she saw the drugstore up ahead.

Larry handed Emogene a five-dollar bill. "Pack of Lucky's, don't forget the matches, and something for yourself and the boys."

The air in the drugstore felt blue and frosted over just like the "Kool Inside" sign displayed by the entrance promised. She left the boys at the candy aisle, headed for the cosmetic counter.

She pulled the tester lipsticks from their cases, made tiny marks on the back of her wrist the way she'd seen Rosa Lee do. A woman behind the counter in a white pharmacy coat eyed her suspiciously. "You need some help?"

Emogene looked at the clerk's gleaming red mouth. "My mother wants some red lipstick," she said, glad for the screen of Rosa Lee's sunglasses. She wiped her hand on her shorts, thinking about the bigness of her lie. She pictured her mother, her thin disappointed mouth painted red, like a paper cut.

"What shade?" The clerk put on the eyeglasses dangling from her neck on a silver chain, turned to the shelves behind her.

"I don't know. "She scanned the names on the lipstick displays. "Something from Revlon." "How about *Red Satin?* It's a very popular shade. The clerk moved down to the other end of the counter, her frosted nail running lightly along the row of small foil-covered boxes. "Last tube, you're in luck." She smiled, handed Emogene the lipstick. "You can pay for that up front."

Emogene found the boys waiting by the register, their gum and sour balls on the counter. "Go on out to the car."

"What'd you get?" Larry Anthony asked.

"Never mind about that. Go get in the car."

At the sunglasses display she put on the lipstick. The color smeared outside the line of her lips. She tried using the tip of her little finger to wipe it off, but a red stain stayed on the skin around her mouth.

"Emogene!" Martin Wendall's shrill voice broke her concentration. Her finger slipped, making a red line down her chin. "My daddy wants to know are you planning on taking all day in here?" He grabbed her shorts, pulling her toward the door. She ran the back of her hand across her mouth and the blurred print of her lips appeared on her skin. She rubbed at the color with her other hand. The red sank into her pores, holding fast as a tattoo.

"Emogene got fireballs," Martin Wendall said, climbing over Larry Anthony.

"Did not." Emogene handed Larry his cigarettes and change. His fingers cupped around hers to catch the coins. She pulled her hand back, passed the boys their candy.

"What happened to your mouth then?" Larry Anthony hung over the front seat to get a better look.

Larry gassed the car. "Sit down, I'm pulling out." Larry Anthony fell against the back seat.

Emogene cut her eyes to the side. A lit cigarette dangled from Larry's fingers. Exhaled smoke hung around his face making him squint. She smelled his breath, soured from the beer he had drunk earlier. She tried to see Rosa Lee beside him, the full skirt of her pink dress spread out on the seat, her arm draped behind him, but Larry was all wrong. Rosa Lee belonged with somebody different, somebody like the photograph of Larry on her nightstand.

Rosa Lee's T-Bird was in the driveway. The screen door opened and she pounced down the steps.

"Uh oh." Martin Wendall pulled back from the window. Emogene dropped the sunglasses between the seats.

"Don't worry, boys," Larry said over his shoulder. "I can handle your mother."

"What the hell's this?" Rosa Lee's hands were on her hips. She bent down to look in the window. "I come home, there's nobody here, the house is wide open, and there's no note." She paused, looking over at Emogene. "Didn't I tell you to leave a note on the kitchen table if you left the yard?" Her eyes narrowed. "Have you been in my makeup?"

"I believe that red mouth is from eating fireballs." Larry touched Rosa Lee's cheek. "You ready for a big time tonight, baby doll?"

Rosa Lee pulled back, her mouth set tight. "I'm too worked up to have a good time."

"You didn't have fireballs!" Martin Wendall yelled from the back seat.

"In the house, now, boys," Larry said. "Get your pajamas, let's go." His hand was back on Rosa Lee's face. This time she allowed it.

Emogene opened her door. She caught up to the boys on the steps, hurried them inside. "Go on, do like your daddy said."

She stood by the picture window, hidden by Rosa Lee's velvet drapes. Rosa Lee leaned on the car, her weight shifting from hip to hip in a slow, swaying dance. She stood up suddenly. Larry grabbed her hands, drew her back. She pulled away and started for the house, Larry watching the whole way.

Emogene backed away from the window.

"I just love him so much, I'd love him even if he was in a car wreck and they cut off his arms and legs." Rosa Lee collapsed on the couch in front of the fan. "We fight like cats and dogs but I couldn't love another man like this, it would kill me."

Emogene spun one of the tassels on the drapery tie-back, watched the silken strands spill through her fingers. Maybe Rosa Lee wouldn't notice when she didn't agree with her like usual.

Rosa Lee chose a magazine from the pile beside her, slid a throw pillow under her head. She crossed her bare feet on the frayed arm of the couch. Orange streaks of indoor tanning lotion laced around her ankles.

Martin Wendall charged out of the bedroom, his round belly leading his solid little legs.

"Come give your Mama a kiss." Rosa Lee dropped her magazine, held out her arms. Martin Wendall fell over her; Rosa Lee buried her face in his neck, took a deep whiff.

Larry Anthony pecked Rosa Lee good-bye on the cheek.

"Why don't you run on home, Emogene?" Rosa Lee said. "I'm going to rest a while before I get dressed, wait for the heat to cool off some."

"I just need the bathroom." Inside, Emogene rubbed hard at her lips until a mound of tissues smeared with red filled the wastebasket. She added her new lipstick to the caddy on Rosa Lee's table, spinning the tubes while she waited to hear Larry's car gun down the street.

"See you next Friday," Rosa Lee said from behind her magazine.

Rosa Lee had forgotten about school starting and Emogene let her. Halfway across the lawn Rosa Lee's music started up: "Pretty woman walking down the street, pretty woman, the kind I'd like to meet. Pretty woman, I couldn't help but see that you look lovely as can be, are you lonesome, just like me?"

She eased the porch door open and stood listening. Her knee rested on the swing; her hands pressed against the screen. The needle swerved across the record; Rosa Lee looking for something that better suited her mood.

Emogene held her fingers flat to her nose, inhaled the familiar tang of rust. The other smell, the something else, didn't come.

THE PATH

LAUREN RHEAUME

You'll never guess who I ran into, my brother texted. He was at work. May, a neighbor we'd grown up with, had come into his store and recognized him from his nametag. I shot back a bunch of questions. *What's she up to? Is she married? Does she look the same?* I alternated between staring at the three dots that showed me he was writing back and locking my phone to try and focus on something else. *Did she ask about me?*

I'd sometimes thought about making sense of how my friendship with May ended. After seventeen years, I still felt the tiniest stirrings of guilt. But was I the villain of our story? Was I responsible not only for the end of our friendship, but her exile? I had to go back to the beginning.

▓▓

When there were still trees between our houses, May's father built a path between us. He made a low stone wall on one end and lined the zigzag pattern with logs. I *loved* the path. Down there May and I met and played and broke twigs off of cherry trees to inhale the scent of root beer. We stayed outside for hours, inventing stories about the woods, traipsing among the trees. We crushed purple berries in our

134

hands and never wondered if they were poisonous.

My family and I had moved to the house in July, a few weeks after I turned seven. May was my age and I attended her birthday party in August, clinging to my mother in their yard, quiet. She was louder, laughter billowing away from her body like a cloud. Soon, we were friends. It was natural, our parents arranging us together because of location, age, the circumstances.

Moving wasn't too much of a transition for me. We lived in another part of town beforehand and I'd continue to attend the same school I'd gone to for three years—the private Catholic school in town. May attended the public school in what seemed to me like another, much larger world. In reality, it was now just a few streets away from home.

We spent so much time outside when we were young, running in the prickly grass of summer, sliding down makeshift waterslides made of tarp and hose. At the end of the path we swept the pine needles away and played house, using branches to mark the foundations and rooms. We rode our pink Huffy bikes nowhere in particular, just around, as our residential town didn't offer much except for ice cream joints. For a while she was the only one who knew I had a crush on the boy a street over, who attended my school and who would sometimes ride with us too.

I couldn't even tell her—she guessed.

"Do you like him?" she asked one day, as he walked his bike into the trees on the edge of his backyard, out of earshot. I broke away from my stare into the back of his head, the one I practiced at school, which I thought was clandestine, casual.

"What are you talking about?" I asked, fighting my cheeks from lifting into a smile, and reddening. I kept my eyes on the grass beneath my legs.

"You stare at him all the time. You've fallen off your bike, like, a lot lately. It seems like you like him."

It was true that'd I'd been distracted by him. I pulled clumps of grass vigorously, tore them up, dropped them onto the street. Finally, I nodded, and looked up at her. She smiled and said, "You do!" so loudly that I shushed her.

She kept my secret for me, even though she was braver. A girl like her wouldn't hesitate to admit her feelings, and for that I admired her. But it also unsettled me.

May started to chase that same boy around the neighborhood endlessly. The three of us would be playing and riding and then we'd drop our bikes on the front lawn, chat and stare at the anthills, drag sticks along the pavement. May would initiate the chase, and he would run, while I stood by on my own, watching and poking holes in the dirt. I remember that feeling, the one I couldn't put into words at the time, the growing discomfort I felt around her, when she'd do exactly what she knew would make me uncomfortable. When she'd take what she knew about me and use it to manipulate a situation. This was before I knew the word *manipulation*. It felt a lot like betrayal.

But it wasn't all bad. Early in our friendship, May and I would pretend we were sisters. We'd compare eye color and freckle count and height, but really the thing that tied us together the most was our straight dark brown hair, which we mostly wore down; strands that would always become tangled in the wind or the wind of running. Her hazel eyes looked nothing like my blue ones—her bright white skin and freckled face didn't match my olive-white tone with darker freckles and moles. But we burned in the sun just the same. Every time we somehow scored one of those cheap plastic Best Friends necklaces, the two-for-one heart-shaped ones with the jagged edge through the center, we knew who we'd be sharing it with. We'd stand next to each other and connect the pieces hanging from the string around our necks, forming one complete heart.

I once told my parents that I was afraid May would hit me. I didn't remember this fact until my mother mentioned it many years later, but upon reflection I have hazy memories of playing with her dolls in her bright pink bedroom, and feeling backed into a corner. Whether we were at my house or hers, May was always the one deciding the game, the situation, which dolls I could touch and animate. I can imagine a sunny afternoon when I was sick of the restrictions she placed on me. I can see myself finally grabbing the Barbie with the prettiest, longest hair, the one I always admired when I was over, and can see May snatch it from me with widened eyes and a yelp, see her raise the doll above our heads like she was going to smash it into my face. But of course she wouldn't do it. She might ruin the doll in the process.

And yet, May challenged me in ways my other friends didn't. She was energetic and talkative, which contrasted with my shy, inward nature. My mother's solution to my shyness was to put me in dancing school when I was nine. I hated it at first, so many new faces, a militant dance teacher, I could barely keep up with the steps. I was always the tall one back then, and I stuck out in the mirror at the front of the room. But soon I was leaving class energized and alive—expressive. For May it wasn't enough to express, it was to *impress*, it was to be the best at everything. She became a singer, an actress, a performer of all kinds. Dance was special, because it was independent of May. I was emerging, ever slowly. But May had emerged a long time before. She'd come over and tell me all about the play she was in, the solo she had, bust into the show tunes she couldn't stop singing. Despite being annoyed by these outbursts, I was partly inspired by her when I auditioned for the solo in my children's church choir when I was ten. I became so confident that if May could do it, so could I. But I bombed, and the part went to another close friend of mine from school. I couldn't help feeling embarrassed for even trying.

One day soon after, May decided we should have a singing contest, and that my mother should be the judge.

My mother said, "Oh, I think I know who's going to win this," with a sly grin at May. And she did win, which wasn't surprising—

after all, she was the one taking singing lessons and belting out songs constantly. I remember feeling pained by that comment nonetheless—*didn't I even have a chance?* But perhaps my mother was reading into why May would propose such a competition. When May would come over, before coming upstairs to my room, she'd talk with my mother as though she was visiting *her* instead of me. My mother found it strange, constantly edging May toward the steps, saying *go play now*, but May never really took the hint. The next time she was over she'd be chatting up my parents, just like last time.

My friendship with May was drastically different during the summer, when we weren't constantly separated because we attended different schools. During the school year we'd have arguments or disagreements but then they'd cool off in the distance; the flames of tension were never strong enough to truly catch and explode. She'd keep the topic of conversation on herself, she bragged and bragged and couldn't stop talking. In those moments, I'd either tell her I needed to go home or I'd think that *soon enough*, I'd be going back to school and I'd see all my other friends, who weren't quite as aggressive and self-obsessed.

But the distance made us more special to each other, an object of interest, curiosity. A friend that none of our other friends had.

▦▦

We stopped using the path sometime around seventh grade, the year I transferred to her public school from the Catholic one I attended since I was five. When I first heard the news of this change, I was angry, and wrote in my journal that May was *not* my friend—I was being sent to a friend-less place. I wrote this probably because sometimes the distance of going to separate schools provided perspective in my young mind—I didn't always feel *good* around May and what did that mean about our friendship?

And yet, a few days later I was writing about how she was making me laugh and out of sheer self-preservation, we became close again over the summer. We fell out of the habit of taking the path on the

138

way to or from each other's houses. We played in it less and less, but sometimes I'd hover on my side of it, sit on the stones near the opening in the trees and think. By that time, the path had started to become overgrown, the logs seeping into the ground with rot, tree branches becoming snarled and twisted together.

So in September, instead of taking the path I'd cross my dew-covered lawn in the mornings and May and I would meet in front of the trees to walk to school together. We'd find her friends waiting outside under the overhang and talk in the few minutes before the bell. I'd attended school with roughly the same twenty-five kids the previous seven years—I missed my friends and was scared about going to a school three times larger, where I didn't know anyone but May. She was my lifeline. I was glad to have her, even though I was placed in a different classroom. Her friends became my friends.

I was navigating the halls with bulky braces on my teeth and enormous glasses covering my face and because I was used to uniforms, I had little sense of what a girl my age should wear to school. Nothing fit right—I either cloaked myself in baggy sweaters or felt I was too exposed, restricted by clothes that were too tight in the wrong places, T-shirts sliding upwards if I bent over to tie my shoes. May's closet was full of her carefully curated style. She'd always had perfect teeth and perfect vision; she always seemed completely comfortable in her skin.

One of these mornings under the overhang, a month or so into the year, her friends, Kelly and Sarah, ventured to ask, *So, what do you think of her?*

It felt like a trap. My own misgivings about May choked me from speaking—I was unsure of the right move. May was several feet away, talking to another group of classmates. I looked at one girl, then the other, and said I liked her, that we'd been friends for a long time. They rolled their eyes in that pre-teen way, and said *she annoys us, we don't want to be friends with her anymore.*

I couldn't breathe a sigh of relief for the validation I felt. It was coupled with fear and suspicion and the fact that she was my only friend there.

I told Kelly and Sarah snippets of what I found annoying about May—the constant tapping of her feet, the random bursts into song, the focusing and maintaining of the topic of conversation on herself. Her pushiness and competitiveness and endless talking. I didn't realize we were galvanizing ourselves against her until it was too late. When May joined back up with our group, Kelly announced it: "We don't want to be friends with you."

"What?" May asked, and when she made eye contact with me, I looked away. I wasn't sure about what we were doing. I didn't trust Kelly and Sarah. But I also didn't want to be aligned with May when I already had so many issues with her, and if she was going to be outcast, I didn't want to be outcast with her. The bell rang and I went off to my classroom, sneaking another unsure glimpse in her direction. Her face was red but it often was—I couldn't read it, and I'm sure she couldn't read mine either. I didn't know whether or not I should expect to see her at the end of the day, for the walk home, but that afternoon she was nowhere to be found. I felt a churning in my gut, and I took an extra few glances around for her before I walked home with Sarah instead.

This prompted *The Meeting*. May's mother called my mother and requested we come over to discuss the situation. It was the following afternoon, those precious few hours between the school day and supper.

My mother was hesitant, but relented. When we arrived, May was not in sight. Her mother led us to the blue rug room, the area in their house meant for special occasions, the off-limits place we could never play in. My mother and I were asked to sit in stiff, uncomfortable armchairs and we weren't asked to remove our shoes, which was the rule. It all felt like trouble.

May's mother addressed me, asked me what happened, why was May upset? *Who started this?* She had to know it couldn't have come from only me. I was the quiet girl at her breakfast table during sleepovers—*don't you talk?* she and her husband had asked, but they were used to May, her never-ending chatter. I told her about May's other two friends, the questions they asked me, and how I initially responded.

"Look," my mother chimed in, "Lauren's new to the school, and she's going to be making her own friends."

"And destroying May's friendships in the process?"

"This isn't something she started. Those other friends had their own opinions and feelings before Lauren came to the school."

"Then why would things change only when she's added to the picture?" she asked. And I couldn't blame her for that question—I had no response. I found myself looking to the ceiling slightly. May must have been upstairs in her bedroom, right above us. Was she listening? May's mother shifted and asked me, "Do you really want to go along with this?" She tried to convince me to remain friends with her daughter, but I balked, silent. In that blue room with our mothers during *The Meeting*, I found myself fantasizing about a life free from May, and I immediately felt better. I could have a life where I wasn't under her control, where I didn't have to listen to her rules, her stories, her songs—where I didn't feel pushed around by her. Nothing anyone said could force me back. That feeling of relief was the only thing giving me a shred of confidence in the decision.

"I have an appointment," my mother said, "so we really have to be going now." We left, got into the car and drove to the jeweler before they closed, to pick up a watch that needed a new battery. As far as I know, our mothers never brought up the subject again.

I've gone back to old journals to find out more about this situation. I was a religious diarist all through this time, but there are notable gaps that I did not document. I often kept things private, even from myself. If I wrote it down, I could be discovered. Sometimes, May and I would write together, which was another reason to keep the details of our friendship out of those pages. On

141

my old hardcover diary, glitter nail polish artwork covering animated versions of Pocahontas and John Smith on the front, is a note from her on the top edges of the pages, near the binding. *Hi! From May*, she wrote. I never scratched it out.

Afterward, when I went to write, there was an unavoidable relic of our friendship reminding me that she'd been left behind. Every so often, I would get real with myself, writing things like "you aren't always going to have your friends there or anyone there to stick up for you. You are going to have to fend for yourself." I was still the awkward quiet girl, longing for my old school, my old friends. I jumped from girl to girl to girl, declaring a new best friend every other week, only to run into drama they were involved with, or outright rejection. My mother expressed concern over whether I was hanging with the right crowd, or *any* crowd. "I guess I'll invite a girl or two over to show her I have some friends," I wrote.

But still, I was haunted by what we had done to May. I was afraid I'd suffer the same fate—the tenuous friendships I was making were marred by overt bullying I wasn't used to. Preteen girls trying to assert their place in life by laying claim to a certain seat in classrooms, bored bullies kicking my calves in the hallways. "I feel like May," I wrote, "I'm just waiting for the day when those people rat me out. Treat me like a piece of shit like we did to her." And later, "I need some friends."

I wrote, "I need a girl to talk to."

I asked my mother recently about this time, seventeen years later—could she remember anything else about that meeting we had with May's mother, how we felt we were on trial? Her memory wasn't much clearer than mine. She said, "You know, during the very first conversation I ever had with May's mother, when both our families had just moved, she told me that the entire reason they moved was because at their old house, May had issues with the girl next door."

"That can't be right," I said, "Are you serious?"

"I am. And I couldn't help myself from reacting. Her mother

could tell I was shocked, my face betrayed my emotions."

"How does a six-year-old have such a bad relationship with another person that it forces her family to move?" I asked, to which neither of us had an answer. Was May too smart for her own good—was she bored and that's what drove her to manipulate me all the time? Did May not get enough attention? Her parents seemed to give her everything she could ever want. But I found her mother intense and strange. Even I knew that the constant cycle of new things was nothing compared to a mother's attention and love.

After eighth grade we went on to separate high schools. We never reconnected. I'd see her around, of course—we were still neighbors. But we didn't talk. Every time my volleyball team played a game at her high school I'd look around for her, but our paths never crossed.

I sometimes find myself thinking of May, and wonder if it's guilt I should feel after all these years. I've thought about how I abandoned her—how I cut her out of my life alongside two of her other friends—how does a person recover from something like that? But ending my friendship with her gave me the courage to end future manipulative friendships and relationships. So many of the friendships I've formed in life were due to proximity and convenience and alphabetical arrangements in classrooms. Of the friends I made in those last two years before high school, only one of them stuck.

My brother ran into her again a few weeks after his initial text, at the annual fall festival in our hometown. That's when I finally got the full story. She's married and has an energetic two-year-old, whom she mostly tried to keep track of while they were talking. When she asked about me, he told her that I'd moved to Boston, that I worked downtown. I later found her online and saw a picture of her and her daughter, their mouths open in jubilant smiles. It was nice to see her in such an obvious expression of love. I felt happy for her. And I felt the mildest lifting of guilt.

Over the years since that day in seventh grade, though both of our families still live in those houses, all signs of the path have been erased. Developers came in and took most of our trees away. The berries in the brush and root beer-scented branches were taken, too. They built a road between our homes, the fresh tar darker than our street, and soon enough there were houses in place of the woods we played in when we were young.

HOUSED

LARRY FLYNN

They made | our dollhouse
with | a place | for everything | and
everything | in its place:

    the master bedroom | framed by knotted flower stems |
    strung in chaotic | order |

    on worn wallpaper | and quilted in | forlorn fabric | on the
    | plastic bed.

    the kitchen smelling | of burnt chocolate | cookies served
    on | fine plastic | with

    lace trimmings | beneath a butter | knife that pricks |
    enough to bleed.

    the living room consumed | by blue light | hazing | a family
    of four | ordered

    in decrescendo | from poppa bear to baby | bear, unable to
    | see for themselves,

the bathroom tub
              overflowing   floating bubbles
        breaking through
                                ceilings
              and walls,   all sides,
        drowning the knives
                              and washing away
        fake flowers
              burnt cookies
                    and blue lights.   This is

        the absence of walls,

the house
we make.

LETTERS OF SUPPORT

VERN SMITH

It's eleven fifty-six when I hear a cat stubbornly meowing outside my apartment. Hiking up my house shorts, I get out of bed and make for the door, peeling back a piece of tape covering my peephole. I put it there so people can't look in on me.

From my fisheye view, I see the little silver number from the far end of the hall. She is on a sky-blue leash and holding firm to the carpet with her claws. Pulling the other way, her owner, the anti-smoking lady, shushes.

Whatever the anti-smoking lady is doing outside my door with her cat at minutes to midnight, the little silver number continues hanging onto the carpet fibers, wailing. I'm no authority on these things, but I believe that she calls to the two tabbies living across the hall. I look on as Natalia Cauzillo opens her door. Holding her blood-red smoking jacket together, she ignores the anti-smoking lady, bending down to say hello to the little silver number. That's when her tabbies escape to do the same.

"Nosey," the anti-smoking lady says, chin nodding to her silver cat.

Natalia wrinkles her face, bringing severe bangs closer to her brows. "And yet I can't help but think that the little thing gave you away."

The anti-smoking lady has been at it since last year. It was December when she put a sign on her door demanding that there be no smoking within fifty meters. Although I didn't think it was enforceable – like you can't just type something up, tape it to your door, and declare it law, even in Canada – I knew right away that her missive would put me on the bubble, given that she lives fifty-six yards south of Natalia's door and mine. I've paced it off, but have yet to convert my findings to metric.

Whatever, I haven't seen anyone smoking in the halls since they threw out the poor old lady three doors down and across. She used to fall asleep while she was smoking. And yes, the fire department was involved on a number of occasions. Unless she died, I'm pretty sure they brought her somewhere she can't smoke at all.

As for the anti-smoking lady, her sign was ripped in half before Christmas. The remaining words stood in martyrdom through the holidays until she replaced it with a letter of support from a nearby neighbor, who, apparently, had just spent their first New Year's Eve in downtown Toronto and did not appreciate the array of smokables consumed. Since then, it's been one scrawled warning after another for fellow tenants to stop smoking in their own homes.

From what I understand, smoke had been detected on or about Labor Day, hence four more letters of support, one of which claimed 614 was firing bottle rockets off his balcony, more smoke. Yesterday, I noticed a new communiqué including allegations against unnamed residents revolving around the burning of even more volatile substances.

Now, I can't say for sure that the anti-smoking lady is sniffing under our doors, just that it seems odd to find her there trying to pull her cat in the opposite direction at minutes to midnight on a Friday. I mean, I either can't stop smoking or I won't, but at least it keeps me from lurking around like that.

"Have you been smoking pot?" the anti-smoking lady wants to know.

"Here we go," I whisper to myself.

"I'm burning incense," Natalia says, looking past the anti-smoking lady and at my door.

"Incense?"

"Yes, incense," Natalia says, reconnecting with the anti-smoking lady. "It's called Love. An aphrodisiac."

"But you're alone."

"What's that supposed to mean?"

"It means you've been smoking pot in there," the anti-smoking lady says, pointing her index past Natalia and into 626, then to her own feet. "And you've been smoking tobacco out here."

"First, I've never smoked anything in the hall," Natalia says. "Second, whatever you think I'm doing in here, you've got to be kidding. Get drunk, get a hobby, or get yourself off – I don't care – just get going."

"I can see it in your eyes," the anti-smoking lady says. "You've been smoking pot."

That said, she finally has the little silver number heading south. As they pull away, Natalia says she might as well get her money's worth, seeing as how she's getting the blame anyway, and reaches into her pocket, retrieving a Zippo and a pack of cigarettes from her smoking jacket. She lights one, hits it, blowing smoke after the lady, then shoo-shooing her tabbies inside. Taking a long drag, she exhales, letting go of a lovely plume in the flickering hallway light. When I hear the anti-smoking lady let herself in fifty-six yards away, her lock clicking, Natalia takes another hit. Exhaling more dramatically this time, she smiles, focusing on my peephole.

"Are you cold?"

Seconds pass as I cling to my silence.

"I can hear you breathing," she says, still looking. "And it sounds like you're cold."

ABOUT THE CONTRIBUTORS

Daisy Bassen

Daisy Bassen is a poet and practicing physician who graduated magna cum laude from Princeton University's Creative Writing Program and completed her medical training at The University of Rochester and Brown. Her work has been published in *Oberon, The Delmarva Review, The Sow's Ear,* and *Tuck Magazine* as well as multiple other journals. She was a semi-finalist in the 2016 Vassar Miller Prize in Poetry, a finalist in the 2018 Adelaide Literary Prize, and the winner of the So to Speak 2019 Poetry Contest. She was nominated for the 2019 *Best of the Net Anthology* and was doubly nominated for a 2019 *Pushcart Prize*. She lives in Rhode Island with her family.

Mike Bendzela

Mike Bendzela has published fiction in several North American periodicals and anthologies, including *Pushcart Prize XVIII* and *Men On Men 7*. More recently, his work has appeared *in Stonecoast Review, Ilanot Review,* and *Meat for Tea*. A parable, "Fertility," won *Two Sisters* Writers & Publishers Flash Fiction Contest, January 2019. His novella *February* was published by *Running Wild Press* in 2019. He teaches at the University of Southern Maine and lives with his husband on a small orchard and farm.

Annabelle Blomeley

Annabelle Blomeley is a freshman at the University of Alabama and an alumna of the Alabama School of Fine Arts. Her work has been published numerous times and she is a scholarship recipient of the Alabama Writer's Forum.

Jake Branigan

Jake Branigan teaches a fiction class at Virginia Commonwealth University, where he received his MFA. A former managing editor at *Blackbird*, he has published fiction in *Blue River*, co-wrote the short film and Apple Music Exclusive "The Beautiful and Damned," and was a contributor at the 2018 Sewanee Writers' Conference.

Stephanie K. Brownell

Stephanie K Brownell is an interdisciplinary writer, artist and educator holding an MFA in Playwriting from Boston University. Stephanie was a 2018 Sewanee Writers' Conference Tennessee Williams Scholar as well as a recipient of the National Partners of the American Theatre Playwriting Excellence Award. Stephanie's plays, poems, and fiction have been published or are forthcoming through *Typishly Literary Journal, formercactus, Crab Fat Magazine, Santa Ana River Review,* and more. Stephanie lives in Boston, teaching creative writing at Grub Street Writing Center and producing theatre with Artists' Theater of Boston.

David Capps

David Capps is a philosophy professor at Western Connecticut State University. Recently his poems have been featured in *Peacock Journal, All the Sins, Portrait of New England, Cagibi,* among others. He lives in Hamden, CT, with a luxurious Maine Coon named Purrbasket.

Sarah Carleton

Sarah Carleton writes poetry, edits fiction, tutors English, plays the banjo, raises her son and makes her husband laugh in Tampa, Florida. Her poems have appeared in numerous publications, including *Off the Coast, The Binnacle, Cider Press Review, Nimrod, Chattahoochee Review, Tar River Poetry, Crab Orchard Review* and *New Ohio Review.*

Ann Casapini

Ann Casapini has been a yoga and meditation instructor since 1995. She also loves to write, sing and dance salsa! She has been published in *Still Point Arts Quarterly, Dunes Review, The Sun, Awakened Voices Blog: The Nightingale, Medusa's Laugh Press: Microtext Anthology 3, Intima: A Journal of Narrative Medicine, Scablands Books: Weird Sisters,* and *The Afterlife of Discarded Objects: A collective storytelling project.* Ann is a repeat contributor to both *Read650.com* and *Military* Experience & the Arts' on-line journal: *As You Were.* Ann studies writing with Steve Lewis and lives in Tuckahoe, NY.

Eileen Cunniffe

Eileen Cunniffe writes mostly nonfiction and often explores identity and experience through the lenses of travel, family and work. Her writing has appeared in three other anthologies and in many literary journals, including *Still Point Arts Quarterly, bioStories, Hofstra Windmill, Bluestem Magazine* and *The RavensPerch.* Eileen's essays have been recognized with Travelers' Tales Solas Awards and the Emrys Journal 2013 Linda Julian Creative Nonfiction Award.

Ann Cwiklinski

Ann Cwiklinski started writing short stories about ten years ago, while raising four children in rural Pennsylvania. Her stories have won first prize at *The Baltimore Review, CentralPA Magazine,* and Yorkfest, a local arts festival, and have also appeared (or are forthcoming) in *pacificREVIEW, Minerva Rising, The Flexible Persona,* and *Belletrist Magazine.*

Liz DeGregorio

Liz DeGregorio is a writer and editor living in New York City. Her fiction has been published in *BUST Magazine*, and three of her poems appeared in *Indie Blu(e)* Publishing's *Smitten: This Is What Love Looks Like* anthology. Her flash fiction has appeared in *82 Review* and *Ruminate Magazine*.

Johanna DeMay

Johanna's parents left the US during the political turmoil of the 1950's. She spent her childhood in Mexico City and began writing to bridge the gap between her two languages, two cultures. As an adult she returned to the US and settled in New Mexico. After a 40 year career as a self-employed artist she now divides her time between writing and volunteering with the immigrant community. Her poems have appeared in *Border Senses, Poem, Passager,* and other journals.

K. Shawn Edgar

We are a Super Organism growing in spacetime. As a tiny cluster of cells within this organism, K. Shawn Edgar lives in Oregon. Since receiving a renal transplantation from the galactic Oregon Health and Science University nephrology wizards, the Greater Portland Metropolitan Area is K. Shawn's ever-present Mother Ship. Bicycles, soluble fiber, and poetry transfusions are ongoing.

Larry Flynn

Larry Flynn teaches humanities at Culver Academies in Indiana and writes stories, poetry, and creative non-fiction. He earned an M.S. in journalism from Northwestern University and produced a documentary on the diverse veteran's community in Aurora, Illinois, which was nominated for a regional Emmy. His writing has been published in *The Petigru Review* (nominated for a Pushcart Prize), *Sports Illustrated,* and other greater-Boston newspapers.

Célèste Fohl

Célèste's is thrilled to be published again in *Crack the Spine*, which featured her essay "Family Style" in issue 250. Her work has also appeared in *Gravel* and several indie-press anthologies. Most recently, she contributed the essay "What We Don't Talk About When We Talk About Gilmore Girls" to the book *The Women of Amy Sherman-Palladino*. Célèste earned her BA in poetry from The University of Cincinnati and her MFA in nonfiction from Lesley University. Now in her 30s, Célèste lives with her husband and daughter in a single-family home. She does, however, still share a common gutter with the house next door.

D. Dina Friedman

D. Dina Friedman is the author of two award-winning young adult novels, *Escaping Into the Night* (*Simon and Schuster*) and *Playing Dad's Song* (*Farrar, Straus, Giroux*) as well as one chapbook of poetry, *Wolf in the Suitcase* (*Finishing Line Press*). She has received two Pushcart Prize nominations and published in many literary journals including *Lilith, Negative Capability, The Sun, Common Ground Review, San Pedro River Review, Steam Ticket, Oyez Review, Mount Hope, New Plains Review, Blue Stem, Red Booth Review, Bloodroot, Anderbo,* and *Rhino*. Her short fiction has also been included in two *Darkhouse Books* anthologies: *Descansos,* and *What We Talk about When We Talk About It: Variations on the Theme of Love*.

Jessica Lynne Furtado

Jessica Lynne Furtado is a poet, photographer, & librarian. Her visual work has been featured in *Muzzle Magazine, PANK, Pretty Owl Poetry, Waxwing,* and elsewhere. Find more of her writing in *apt, Rogue Agent,* and *Stirring,* among others.

Dean Gessie

Dean Gessie is a Pushcart-nominated author and poet who has won multiple international prizes. Dean won the Angelo Natoli Short Story Award in Australia and the Half and One Literary Prize in India. Dean also won the *Bacopa Literary Review* Short Story Competition in Florida, the *Enizagam* Poetry Contest in Oakland, California, the *Two Sisters* Short Story Contest in New Mexico and the After Dinner Conversation Short Story Competition in Arizona. Elsewhere, Dean won the short story contest at the Eden Mills Writers Festival in Canada and he was selected for inclusion in The Sixty Four Best Poets of 2018 by *Black Mountain Press* in North Carolina. In addition, Dean won second prize (of 2000+ submissions) in the Short Story Project New Beginnings competition in New York and his short story made the shortlist (of 2800+ submissions) for the Alpine Fellowship Prize in Stockholm, Sweden.

Dave Gregory

Dave Gregory is a Canadian writer who worked on cruise ships and sailed around the world for nearly two decades. He is an Associate Editor with *Exposition Review* and a Fiction Reader for *Gigantic Sequins*. His work has appeared in numerous literary publications including *Exile: The Literary Quarterly, Firewords,* and *The Sunlight Press.*

Rebekah Keaton

Rebekah Keaton has a PhD in literature from Michigan State University and is an English Professor at Niagara County Community College. She teaches composition, American literature and creative writing. She also coordinates the *On the Edge Poetry Series*. Her work has appeared in a variety of journals, including *Slipstream Magazine, Blueline, Rust+Moth, Common Ground Review,* and *PoemMemoirStory,* and her poetry has been nominated for a Pushcart Prize.

Travis M. Kiger

Travis was born in Thibodaux, LA, and grew up in a lot of places. He has an MFA from the University of Tampa and teaches Literature and Writing at Keiser University. His work has appeared in *Cleaver Magazine, Hobart, Bull Men's Fiction,* the *Dead Mule School of Southern Literature, Bridge Eight Magazine, pioneertown* and elsewhere. When he isn't talking about reading and writing, he's teaching his son to hold the bat with two hands.

Christine Kindberg

Christine Kindberg grew up in Peru, Chile, Panama, Kentucky, and North Carolina. She studied at Wheaton College and has an MFA from Queens University of Charlotte. She now lives in the Chicago suburbs, where she works as a Spanish-language editor at Tyndale House Publishers. When not reading or writing, she can probably be found running or cooking for friends. You can find out more about her novel *The Means That Make Us Strangers* and her other published works on ChristineKindberg.com.

Sally K. Lehman

Sally K Lehman is the author of the novels *In The Fat, The Unit – Room 154,* and *Living in the Second Tense.* Her novel *The Last Last Fight* will be coming out from *Black Bomb Books* in 2020. She has edited three anthologies and her work can be found in several literary magazines including *Lunch Ticket, The Coachella Review,* and *Another Chicago Magazine.* She has an M.A. and an M.F.A. in Creative Writing from Wilkes University where she worked as Managing Editor for *River & South Review.* She lives in the Portland, Oregon area.

Rosaleen Lynch

Rosaleen Lynch, an Irish community worker and writer in the East End of London, pursues stories whether conversational, literary or performed. Published online and in print, including *City of Stories, The Word for Freedom* and most recently the *Short Édition* story dispensers and *Jellyfish Review.*

James B. Nicola

James B. Nicola's poems and prose have appeared in the *Antioch, Southwest, Green Mountains,* and *Atlanta Reviews; Rattle; Barrow Street; Tar River;* and *Poetry East.* He has been the featured poet in *Westward Quarterly* and *New Formalist.* A Yale graduate, he has earned a Dana Literary Award, two Willow Review awards, a People's Choice award (from *Storyteller*), and six Pushcart nominations—from *Shot Glass Journal, Parody, Ovunque Siamo, Lowestoft Chronicle,* and twice from *Trinacria*—for which he feels both stunned and grateful. His nonfiction book *Playing the Audience* won a *Choice* award. His poetry collections are *Manhattan Plaza* (2014), *Stage to Page: Poems from the Theater* (2016), *Wind in the Cave* (2017), *Out of Nothing: Poems of Art and Artists* (2018), and *Quickening: Poems from Before and Beyond* (2019).

Brandon Noel

Brandon Noel (He/Him), lives in Northeastern Ohio and has worked as a machinist for the last ten years while writing on his breaks and brief moments of down time. His work often focuses on working-class life, and has appeared in *Door-Is-A-Jar, YSU's The Jenny, Gordon Square Review & The Esthetic Apostle.* He has two published poetry collections: *Mongrel* (2015) and *Infinite Halves* (2017), and facilitates a monthly writers group called, "The Makeshift Poets". Brandon turned 33 last December and raises two daughters, ages 10 and 5, with their mother.

Lauren Rheaume

Lauren Rheaume is an essayist. She's a staff member at GrubStreet in Boston and a graduate of the Essay Incubator program. Her work has been published at *Boston Accent, Punctuate.,* and *GrubWrites.* You can find her online at @laurenxelissa.

Vern Smith

Vern Smith is the author of *The Green Ghetto* (*Run Amok Books*), a new novel set on Detroit's prairie. *Broken Pencil* – Canada's guide to alternative culture – calls it "a model for modern westerns." Vern's fiction has appeared in *Concrete Forest: The New Fiction of Urban Canada* (*McClelland & Stewart*), a handful of anthologies, and several magazines.

Judith Turner-Yamamoto

Judith Turner-Yamamoto's awards include a 2018 Artistic Excellence Fellowship from the Ohio Arts Council, 2018 Bridport Prize for the Short Story, short list; residency fellowships from VCAA and Fundacíon Valparaiso; 2016 Seán O'Faoláin Short Story Prize, long list; Finalist; 2016 Fish International Short Story Prize, Finalist; Manchester Fiction Prize, Short List; StoryQuarterly Scholar, Sewanee Writers' Conference; the Thomas Wolfe Fiction Prize, the Virginia Governor's Screenwriting Award, two Fellowships from the Virginia Commission on the Arts, and the Moving Words Poetry Prize, Arlington County, Virginia Arts Council. Poems and prose have appeared in *StorySOUTH, The American Literary Review, The Mississippi Review,* and many others.

Ellen Weeren

Ellen Weeren's work has been published by the *Kenyon Review* (online), *Liars' League, The Hong Kong Review,* and *Stonecoast Review.* She's the recipient of the George Mason 2019 Outstanding Graduate Student Award (MFA Fiction), the Porches Writing Fellowship, the Dan Rudy Fiction Award, the Marjorie Kinnear Sydor Award in Literary Citizenship, and the *Kenyon Review's* Novel Writing Workshop Peter Taylor Fellowship. TripBase twice recognized her blog about living in India as one of the top 10 best travel blogs. Ellen earned her MFA (fiction) from George Mason University.

Will Wells

Will Wells has published three full-length poetry collections, most recently *Odd Lots, Scraps & Second-hand, Like New*, which won the 2016 *Grayson Books* Poetry Prize and was published in April 2017. His previous collection, *Unsettled Accounts*, won the *Hollis Summers* Poetry Prize and was published by *Ohio Univ./Swallow Press* in 2010. An earlier volume won the Anhinga Prize in Poetry.

Stephen Scott Whitaker

Stephen Scott Whitaker is a member of National Book Critics Circle, and managing editor for *The Broadkill Review*. His poetry, fiction, and essays have appeared in *Oxford Poetry, The Scores, Anderbo, Grub Street, Miracle Monocle* and others. His novel of weird fiction, *Mulch*, is forthcoming from *Montag Press*. He lives on the Eastern Shore of Virginia with his family.

Peri Dwyer Worrell

Peri Dwyer Worrell grew up on a Puerto Rican street in New York, gaining a keen appreciation of diversity, tolerance, and taking no crap from anyone. After 30 years as a physician, Peri expatriated to Latin America. Peri now writes books, poetry, and travel blogs, and edits science articles freelance.

CRACK THE SPINE LITERARY MAGAZINE

Crack the Spine loves the written word. Some might say we're *in* love with the written word. But that's just a silly rumor. We publish diverse and sharp literary works, including flash fiction, micro-fiction, poetry, short stories, and creative non-fiction. We don't care if it's four words or four thousand words, if it's charged with artistry, we want to publish it. Given the choice, we will always select madness over method.

Made in the USA
San Bernardino, CA
02 March 2020